OVR $7...

D1248711

Functionals
and Their Applications

Selected Topics
Including Integral Equations

by Griffith Conrad Evans

DOVER PUBLICATIONS, INC.
NEW YORK

Published in the United Kingdom by Constable & Company, Ltd., 10 Orange Street, London W.C.2.

This Dover edition, first published in 1964, is an enlarged and corrected republication of the work first published by the American Mathematical Society in 1918 as Part I of the *Cambridge Colloquium, 1916*, and includes a Preface, an Appendix, an Index to Authors, and a list of References to Special Terms prepared especially for this edition by the author.

Library of Congress Catalog Card Number: 64-18849

Manufactured in the United States of America

Dover Publications, Inc.
180 Varick Street
New York 14, N. Y.

PREFACE TO THE DOVER EDITION

My Cambridge Colloquium Lectures were delivered in 1916, when many fields of mathematics were opening. Some of them are explored in these lectures, published as a book in 1918.

Mathematics has been defined in various ways. For myself, at least, it is both concrete and abstract. On the one hand it is analytical and has an inherent abstraction that increases as the subject develops. Yet on the other, its sources and aims are governed by intuition and imagination, and it arises all the stronger as it rebounds each time from the earth. "Poincaré était un intuitif" wrote Darboux. Was it partly his memoir on residues of functions of two complex variables that impelled him towards topology? This memoir I have discussed, more comprehensively than in the original edition, in the Appendix to the present publication. Pages 50 and 51 have been revised as necessary to accord with this addition.

Throughout the Lectures I had in mind mostly concrete problems. But even where some problems could have been treated directly, the door was opened to such things as the (abstract) dyadic-vector product of J. W. Gibbs, or P. Lévy's exposition and use of adjointness of integro-differential forms. An account of the progress of abstraction in the field has been given by M. Fréchet, "Pages choisies d'analyse générale" (1953). Of course much was accomplished before 1932, when S. Banach published his "Théorie des opérations linéaires", in which he named Volterra as the founder of Operation Theory. J. Hadamard's "Leçons sur le calcul des variations" was published in 1910, and P. Lévy's "Leçons d'analyse fonctionelle" in 1922, the latter with a second edition in 1951.

Besides the Appendix, I have added in the present publication an Index of Authors and a short list of References to Special Terms. I hope that the volume still represents an introduction to the general field, as well as a 1918 picture of it.

Finally, I wish to thank the Council of the American Mathematical Society for its cordial acquiescence in this republication, and above all Dover Publications, Inc., and Mr. Hayward Cirker, President, for adding this small volume to the collection of its republications, which has added so much to the libraries of students of mathematics, including myself.

GRIFFITH C. EVANS

October, 1963.

AUTHOR'S PREFACE.

Most mathematicians are familiar with that development of the subject of integral equations which is epitomized by the name Hilbert. There are however other domains whose description is not so completely available in book form, which represent nevertheless an expansion of the same circle of fundamental notions, implied in the central theory of integral equations. Volterra's genial concepts, developed during the last thirty years, and outlined in his treatise of 1913, have by contact with the ideas of Hadamard, Stieltjes, Lebesgue, Borel and others, given rise to many new points of view. It is the purpose of the Lectures to select for discussion some of those which appear most to promise further rapid expansion.

A word may be necessary as to the arrangement. In order to make the subject matter accessible to as large a circle of readers as possible, the text in large type has been devised to be intelligible to those who approach the subject for the first time, and may be read by itself. The text in small type comes, on the other hand, closer to the present state of the subject, and may be more suggestive. The author thus hopes to fulfil the avowed purpose of the Colloquium.

Commas in formulæ are omitted when not necessary for clearness; thus $r(\lambda, t)$ is written $r(\lambda t)$ if the meaning is clear from the context.

The author has given references to American mathematicians freely, in order that familiarity with names may stimulate conversation at meetings of the Society, and thereby increase interest in the subject itself.

HOUSTON, TEXAS,
    February, 1918.

G.W.E.
1860–1947

CONTENTS

LECTURE I

FUNCTIONALS, DERIVATIVES, VARIATIONAL EQUATIONS

Continuity of a functional. Derivative of a
functional. Additive and non-additive functionals
of plane curves. Existence of a derivative, additive
functionals *vs.* functions of point sets. Examples
of functional derivatives. Non-additive functionals.

Introduction. Functional derivatives and functional fluxes. Additive functionals of curves in
space. The condition of integrability for additive
functionals. Change of variable. Functionals of
surfaces and hypersurfaces.

The dependence of the Green's function on the
boundary. Adjoint linear functionals. The conditions of integrability. Special equations. The
integrability of the equation for the Green's function. Variational *vs.* integro-differential equations.

Volterra's equation for the Dirichlet integral.
The condition of integrability.

LECTURE II

COMPLEX FUNCTIONALS

Isogeneity and complex vector fluxes. Summary
of the properties of the linear vector function. The
condition of isogeneity.

LECTURE III

IMPLICIT FUNCTIONAL EQUATIONS

LECTURE IV

INTEGRO-DIFFERENTIAL EQUATIONS OF BÔCHER TYPE

LECTURE V

DIRECT GENERALIZATIONS OF THE THEORY OF INTEGRAL EQUATIONS

The equation (G^5). The closure properties C_3 and
C_4. Mixed linear equations. Further developments. The content of the operation J.

    The associative combinations of the first and
    second kinds. The algebra of permutable and
    non-permutable functions. The Volterra relation
    and reciprocal functions. Fredholm's theorem of
    multiplication. Developments in series. Exten-
    sion of analytic functions. Integro-differential
    equations of static type and Green's theorem.
    The method of particular solutions. The Cauchy
    problem for integro-differential equations. Func-
    tions of nullity.

APPENDIX

POINCARÉ THEORY OF INTEGRALS OF FUNCTIONS OF TWO COMPLEX VARIABLES

REFERENCES TO SPECIAL TERMS

Analytic is used in the sense of analytic and
    bounded: holomorphic.
Surfaces are assumed to be orientable.

LECTURE I

FUNCTIONALS, DERIVATIVES AND VARIATIONAL EQUATIONS*

§ 1. FUNDAMENTAL NOTIONS; FUNCTIONALS OF PLANE CURVES

1. Continuity of a Functional. If we have two sets of values x and y, we say that y is a function of x if to every value of x in its set corresponds a value of y. Similarly, if we have a set of functions $\varphi(x)$ given between limits a and b, and a set of values y, we say that y is a functional of $\varphi(x)$ if to every $\varphi(x)$ of the set corresponds one of the values y. This relation we may write in some such form as the following:

$$(1) \qquad\qquad y = y[\varphi(\overset{b}{\underset{a}{x}})].$$

It is an obvious generalization if instead of a functional of $\varphi(x)$, we speak of a functional of a curve (in a plane, or in space), or of a surface. Of special interest are the closed curves. The area inside a closed plane curve, the Green's function of which the point arguments are fixed, and the solutions of boundary value problems in physics are ready examples of functionals of curves or surfaces. The maximum of a function is a functional of that function.

---

* This lecture is based upon the following references:

Volterra, Sopra le funzioni che dipendono da altre funzioni; Sopra le funzioni dipendenti da linee, *Rendiconti della Reale Accademia dei Lincei*, vol. 3 (1887), five notes;
  Leçons sur les fonctions de lignes, Paris (1913), chapters I, II, III.

Hadamard, Sur l'équilibre des plaques élastiques encastrées, *Mémoires présentées à l'Académie des Sciences*, vol. 33.

P. Lévy, Sur les équations intégro-differentielles définissant des fonctions de lignes, *Thèses présentées à la Faculté des Sciences de Paris*, no. d'ordre 1436;
  Sur les équations aux dérivées fonctionelles et leur application à la Physique mathématique, *Rendiconti del Circolo Matematico di Palermo*, vol. 33 (1912);
  Sur l'intégration des équations aux dérivées fonctionelles partielles, *Rendiconti del Circolo Matematico di Palermo*, vol. 37 (1914).

The argument of a functional, if a curve or a surface, may be regarded as having sense; and the value of a functional of a curve will depend therefore generally on the direction in which the curve is taken, and the value of a functional of a surface upon which choice we make for the positive aspect of the surface.

A variable y which depends upon all the values of a continuous function $\varphi(x)$, in a range $a \leq x \leq b$, that is, by means of a relation of the form (1), may for many purposes be considered as a function of an infinite number of variables, e. g., of the values of φ which correspond to the rational values of x. In fact, since this infinity is a denumerable one, the properties of functionals of a continuous function may in a measure be foretold by considering the properties of functions depending upon a finite number of variables and letting that number become infinite.

As an instance, consider the definition of continuity. A function $f(x_1 \cdots x_n)$ is said to be continuous at a point $(x_1^0 \cdots x_n^0)$ if the quantity $|f - f_0|$ can be made as small as desired by taking the quantities $|x_i - x_i^0|$, $i = 1, 2, \cdots, n$, all less than δ, with δ small enough. A similar conception applies to a function of an infinite number of variables,* and therefore to a functional. We shall therefore say that $y[\varphi(x)]_a^b$ is continuous in φ for $\varphi = \varphi_0$ if the limit as δ vanishes of $y[\varphi(x)]$ is $y[\varphi_0(x)]$, where $|\varphi(x) - \varphi_0(x)| < \delta$, $a \leq x \leq b$; in other words, as φ approaches φ_0 uniformly.

2. Derivative of a Functional. The same generalization is not serviceable directly in the extension of the idea of *derivative*. It is therefore from this point of view more convenient to generalize the idea of *differential*—a linear continuous function of the increments of the infinite number of variables thus leading to a linear continuous functional of the increment $\theta(x)$ of $\varphi(x)$. The functional derivative is however itself a natural conception.

In the neighborhood of a value x_0, let $\varphi(x)$ be given a continuous increment $\theta(x)$ which does not change sign: let us write

---

* It may be desirable to replace, in some cases, the quantity δ by $\sigma_i\delta$, $i = 1, 2, \cdots, n$, where the σ_i are given " scale " values (in accordance with E. H. Moore's concept of relative uniformity).

$|\theta(x)| < \epsilon$, in the interval $x_0 - h \leq x \leq x_0 + h$, setting $\theta(x) = 0$ otherwise, and let us form the ratio $\Delta y/\sigma$, where $\sigma = \displaystyle\int_a^b \theta(x)dx$. If this ratio approaches a limit as ϵ and h approach zero in an arbitrary manner, the limit is defined as the functional derivative of $\underset{a}{\overset{b}{y}}[\varphi(x)]$ at the point x_0:

$$(2) \qquad y'[\overset{b}{\underset{a}{\varphi(x)}}\,|\,x_0] = \lim_{\epsilon=0,\,h=0} \frac{\Delta y}{\sigma}.$$

A similar definition applies for the derivative of a functional of a plane curve, as the accompanying diagram shows; the derivative may be denoted by the symbol $y'[C\,|\,M]$, or even $y'(M)$,

Fɪɢ. 1

if there is no ambiguity.   The point M denotes in this connection a point on the curve C.   The quantity σ is considered as positive or negative according as it lies on the same side of the curve, or not, as the positive normal (which we take on a closed curve as directed towards the interior).*

3. Additive and Non-Additive Functionals of Plane Curves. Let C_1 and C_2 be two closed plane curves exterior to each other except for a common portion C', with directions such that C' is traversed in opposite ways on the two curves; and let C_3 be the curve composed of C_1 and C_2 with the omission of C', the

---

* It is not desirable, for what follows, to consider any curves whose running point co-ordinates are not functions of finite variation of a parameter t; in fact we need consider only "standard" curves (see Art. 49). For simplicity of geometrical treatment, we thus make a distinction with respect to generality when the argument of a functional is a curve, instead of a function (see, for instance, Lecture III). The case where the curves have vertices involves no special consideration.

direction following that on the original curves.   If now for every such case the relation

$$(3) \qquad\qquad y[C_1] + y[C_2] = y[C_3]$$

is satisfied, the functional $y[C]$ is said to be *additive*.

If y is an additive functional, Δy will depend merely upon the contour σ, without regard to the rest of the curve C, of which σ represents the distortion.   Evidently then, $y'[C \,|\, M]$ will not depend upon C, but upon the point M alone: *the derivative of an additive functional is merely a point function in the plane.*

Let us give to the points of C a displacement along the normal, of amount $\delta n(M) = \epsilon \psi(M)$, where $\psi(M)$ represents a continuous function of the arc distance along C.   Denote by δy the principal part of the infinitesimal change of y, i. e., the quantity $\epsilon[dy/d\epsilon]_{\epsilon=0}$.   From the definition of functional derivative, we should expect, for an additive functional:

$$(4) \qquad\qquad \delta y = \int_C y'(M)\delta n(M)ds$$

and for a non-additive functional:

$$(5) \qquad\qquad \delta y = \int_C y'[C \,|\, M]\delta n(M)ds,$$

and therefore, for an additive functional:

$$(6) \qquad\qquad y[C_2] - y[C_1] = \int\int y'(M)d\sigma,$$

where the region of integration is the region between C_1 and C_2, $d\sigma$ being given the proper sign at each point; and for a non-additive functional:

$$(7) \qquad\qquad y[C_2] - y[C_1] = \int\int y'[C \,|\, M]d\sigma,$$

where the region is the same as before, and the curves C form a continuous one-parameter family containing C_1 and C_2.

The formulæ (4) and (5) are still valid if the significance of $\delta n(C)$ is slightly generalized, and it is used to denote the variation of C in the sense of the calculus of variations, that is, a quantity of the type $\quad \epsilon \left[\dfrac{\partial \psi(M, \epsilon)}{\partial \epsilon} \right]_{\epsilon=0}.$

If the curve C_1 may be shrunk down to zero without going outside the region of definition, we shall have, for an additive functional, the equation:

$$(6') \qquad y[C] = \iint\limits_{(C)} y'(M)d\sigma.$$

The formulæ (4) to (7) may fail to hold in cases where the derivative does not remain finite, or when the functional itself depends in a special manner upon certain points. These important special cases will be treated, as need arises. But meanwhile it is perhaps desirable to point out sufficient conditions under which formulæ (4) to (7) may be deduced.

4. Existence of a Derivative, Additive Functionals vs. Functions of Point Sets. An additive functional of a curve, $y[C]$, is said to be a *functional of finite variation* if the inequality

$$\Sigma_i \, | \, y[\overline{C_i}] \, | \, < M$$

is satisfied, in which M is a constant, and the closed curves $\overline{C_i}$ are squares (or, with equal generality, rectangles) mutually exterior (except for possible common boundaries), finite or denumerably infinite in number, and all contained in a given finite region. The functional is *absolutely continuous* if the quantity M can be made as small as desired, $< \epsilon$, by taking the sum of the areas of the squares small enough, $< \delta$, irrespective of their position.

It is also convenient to be able to speak of a restricted derivative, and this we define as $\lim\limits_{\overline{C}=0} y[\overline{C}]/(\text{area inside } \overline{C})$, the curve $\overline{C}$ being restricted to a square. In some cases it may be desirable to restrict the curves to circles instead of squares.

We notice at once the relation of the theory of additive functionals to that of functions of point sets. In fact if we define a function $f(\omega)$ of the points in any cell of a square network as the value of $y[\overline{C}]$ for the contour of that square, the value of the function of point sets $f(e)$ will be defined for any point set e which is measurable according to Borel, and if the frontier of e is a standard curve C, we shall have $f(e) = y[C]$. To paraphrase a theorem of De la Vallée-Poussin:[*]

Every additive functional which is continuous and of finite variation defines a continuous additive function of point sets, for point sets measurable according to Borel; the restricted derivatives of the functional and the function are the same wherever they exist.

Hence it follows that *an additive continuous functional of finite variation has a finite derivative (in the restricted sense) at all points except possibly those of a set of measure zero.*

[*] De la Vallée-Poussin, *Transactions of the American Mathematical Society*, vol. 16 (1915), p. 493.

If the functional is *absolutely continuous*, the corresponding function of point sets $f(e)$ will be absolutely continuous for all sets measurable (B). But any set measurable (L) is a set measurable (B) of the same measure plus a set measurable (L) of zero measure. And thus by defining $f(e) = 0$ when e is a set of zero measure (L), $f(e)$ will be defined uniquely for all sets measurable (L), and will be additive and absolutely continuous. It will then have a summable restricted derivative at all points except those of a set of measure zero, and will be itself the integral of that derivative over the set e.* As such, however, it will have a generalized derivative at all points except possibly those of a null set. *Hence if $y[C]$ is an absolutely continuous additive functional it will have a derivative (unrestricted), independent of C, at all points except possibly those of a null set; moreover equation* (6′) *is satisfied*:

$$y[C] = \iint\limits_{(C)} y'(M)d\sigma.$$

Equations (4) and (6) are obvious consequences of (6′).

In the case when the additive functional is merely continuous, there appear in the above equation other terms beside the integral, corresponding to points where the inferior restricted derivative becomes positively infinite, or the superior restricted derivative negatively infinite.

5. Examples of Functional Derivatives. The theorem just enunciated has application in showing the existence of certain differential operators, of which perhaps one example will be sufficient illustration. Consider a function $u(x, y)$ continuous, with its first partial derivatives. The quantity $\int_C \partial u/\partial n \, ds$ will be an additive functional; let us denote its functional derivative, where it exists, by Δu.

If the function $f(x, y)$ is summable, and $u(x, y)$ satisfies the equation

$$(8) \qquad \int_C \frac{\partial u}{\partial n} ds = \iint\limits_{(C)} f(x, y)dxdy$$

for all standard curves, or even for all rectangles, it follows that the functional which we are investigating is absolutely continuous; and therefore Δu exists and satisfies the equation

$$\Delta u = - f(x, y)$$

except at a point set of zero measure. The existence of Δu does not imply the existence of $\partial^2 u/\partial x^2$ or $\partial^2 u/\partial y^2$; and yet, as we shall see in Lecture IV, where $f(x, y)$ is assumed to be continuous, the equation (8), which is equivalent to Poisson's equation, still lends itself to solution.

6. Non-Additive Functionals. The functional derivative of a non-additive functional will not in general be independent of the curve C, and therefore the extension (7) of the result expressed in equation (6) must be obtained.

* De la Vallée-Poussin, Cours d'analyse infinitésimale, Louvain, 1912, vol. 2, p. 102.

Sufficient conditions for this generalization are given by Volterra; it is possible however to reduce them somewhat in extent.*

Consider a functional F depending on all the values of $\varphi(x)$ between a and b. The following theorem may be proved directly. *If for a certain continuous function $\varphi_0(x)$, the functional $F[\varphi(x)]$, continuous in $\varphi(x)$, has a derivative $F'[\varphi(x) \mid \xi]$ for every value of ξ in a certain closed subinterval $a'b'$ of ab (which may be ab itself) that derivative remains limited and continuous throughout $a'b'$.*

To prove this theorem, write $F'[\varphi_0(x) \mid \xi] = t$, and let ξ_1, ξ_2, $\cdots$ be an infinite set of values having ξ_0 as a limiting point, such that

$$\lim_{n=\infty} F'[\varphi_0(x) \mid \xi_n] = t'.$$

We shall assume that t' is finite; the case where t' is infinite occasions an obvious modification of the proof. Let $|t - t'| = p$, and suppose momentarily $p \neq 0$.

Give to $\varphi_0(x)$ a variation of one sign $\theta_1(x)$, of the kind specified in the definition of the derivative, and take ϵ_1 and h_1 so small that we have the inequality

$$|F[\varphi_0(x) + \theta_1(x)] - F[\varphi_0(x)] - t\sigma_1| < \tfrac{1}{2}|p\sigma_1|.$$

We may, however, by taking a variation θ_2, small enough, and about a point ξ_n near enough to ξ_0, and adding to it a variation θ_3, small enough everywhere, yet different from zero at ξ_0, obtain a variation θ_1 for which is satisfied the inequality:

$$|F[\varphi_0(x) + \theta_2(x) + \theta_3(x)] - F[\varphi_0(x) - t'(\sigma_2 + \sigma_3)| < \tfrac{1}{2}|p(\sigma_2 + \sigma_3)|.$$

For since F is assumed to be continuous, the increment θ_3 may be made so small as to affect the difference $F[\varphi_0 + \varphi_2] - F[\varphi_0]$ as little as we please.

But from these two inequalities it follows that

$$|(t - t')(\sigma_2 + \sigma_3)| < |p| |(\sigma_2 + \sigma_3)|,$$

which is a contradiction. Hence $p = 0$, and the theorem is proved.

In order now to obtain the formulæ (5) and (7) we consider as a region for the argument $\varphi(x)$ that included between two given continuous functions $\Phi_1(x)$ and $\Phi_2(x)$, where $\Phi_1(x) < \Phi_2(x)$, in the interval $a \leq x \leq b$, and assume that $F[\varphi]$ is defined for every continuous function in that region, and is continuous. This we call the assumption (α).

In addition to (α) we assume the conditions (λ) (μ), as follows:

(λ) The functional derivative $F'[\varphi(x) \mid \xi]$ exists for every function in the region, and every ξ, $a \leq x \leq b$.

(μ) The ratio $\Delta F/\sigma$ approaches its limit uniformly with respect to all possible functions $\varphi(x)$ and values ξ.

From (α) (λ) (μ) it may be deduced that F' is *continuous in ξ* uniformly for all points ξ and functions φ in the region; and that it is *continuous in ξ and φ* uniformly with respect to ξ and φ, provided that φ is restricted to a family of continuous functions, closed in the sense that the limiting functions are uniform limits.

---

* Evans, *Bulletin of the American Mathematical Society*, vol. 21 (1915), pp. 387–397.

For convenience we denote by (μ_1) that part of the assumption (μ) which requires uniformity with respect to the functional argument alone. From (α) (λ) (μ_1) can be deduced a theorem analogous to Rolle's theorem in the differential calculus:

Let $F[\varphi_1] = F[\varphi_2] = 0$, where $\varphi_1 - \varphi_2$ is a function which does not change sign in the interval ab and is different from zero only in the interval $a'b'$. Then there is a function φ_0, of the pencil determined by φ_1 and φ_2 and a value ξ_0, $a' \leqq \xi_0 \leqq b'$, such that $F'[\varphi_0(x) \mid \xi_0] = 0$.

From this theorem follows the law of the mean, in the same way as in the differential calculus:

LAW OF THE MEAN. *Let $\varphi_1 - \varphi_2$ not change sign in the interval ab, and be different from zero in the sub-interval $a'b'$ (which may be ab itself). There is a function φ_0 of the pencil determined by φ_1 and φ_2, and a value ξ_0, $a' \leqq \xi_0 \leqq b'$, such that*

$$(9) \qquad F[\varphi_2(x)] - F[\varphi_1(x)] = F'[\varphi_0(x) \mid \xi] \int_a^b (\varphi_2(x) - \varphi_1(x))dx.$$

Let us consider now functions $\varphi(x)$ and $\varphi(x) + \omega\psi(x)$, in the given range, ω being an arbitrary parameter whose values are restricted to the neighborhood of $\omega = 0$, and make the assumptions (α) (λ) (μ). We can find an explicit expression for $[dF/d\omega]_{\omega=0}$. In fact, this is easily shown to be of the form

$$(10) \qquad \left(\frac{dF}{d\omega}\right)_{\omega=0} = \int_a^b F'[\varphi(x) \mid \xi]\psi(\xi)d\xi,$$

of which equation (5) is an obvious consequence. Hence also we have:

$$(11) \qquad \left(\frac{dF}{d\omega}\right)_{\omega=\omega} = \int_a^b F'[\varphi(x) + \omega\psi(x) \mid \xi]\psi(\xi)d\xi.$$

From (11) may be deduced the equation

$$(12) \qquad F[\varphi(x) + \psi(x)] - F[\varphi(x)] = \int_a^b F'[\varphi(x) + \theta\psi(x) \mid \xi]\psi(\xi)d\xi,$$

where $0 < \theta < 1$. And from (12) follows the equation (7), already given.

§ 2. FUNCTIONALS OF CURVES IN SPACE

7. Introduction. We are interested in this lecture not so much in the character of the curve, which is the argument of the functional, as in the character rather of the functional relation itself. And so we shall assume without statement, or with slight statement, whatever properties may be needed from time to time in order to make possible the differential and geometric transformations used in the analysis of the functionals. The curves are to be closed, and in particular, each one must be capable of being capped by at least two surfaces which have no points in common except points on the curve, and which enclose a region lying entirely within the region of definition of the functional. Moreover we must be able to pass from one curve of the class to any other by means of a family of curves depending upon a parameter λ, such that the co-ordinates (xyz) of a point on the variable curve will be continuous functions of λ with continuous derivatives up to the second order. We shall consider, of course, only rectifiable curves, since we shall use as a variable the distance s along the curve.

In this lecture we consider merely real functionals of space curves. Lecture II is devoted to their theory as complex numbers.

8. Functional Derivatives and Functional Fluxes. If we take in the neighborhood of a point M, a small portion Δs of the curve C, and give to every point of it a displacement Δx parallel to the x-axis, thus forming a new curve C', the quantity

$$(13) \qquad X[C \,|\, M] = \lim_{\Delta s=0,\, \Delta x=0} \frac{\Delta F[C]}{\Delta s \Delta x},$$

if it exists, is called the derivative of $F[C]$ at the point M in the direction X. Under the conditions of uniform continuity analogous to those specified in the case of plane curves, if we make a displacement of the given curve C by an amount of which the projections on the three axes are respectively $\epsilon\xi(s)$, $\epsilon\eta(s)$, $\epsilon\zeta(s)$, we find for the rate of change of F the value

$$(14) \qquad \left(\frac{\partial F}{\partial \epsilon}\right)_{\epsilon=0} = \int_C (X\xi + Y\eta + Z\zeta)ds.$$

In fact if the points of the curve first take on a displacement parallel to the x-axis of amount $\epsilon\xi(s)$, there will result to $F[C]$ an increment of amount $\Delta F_1 = \epsilon \int_C X\xi ds$, etc. The above formula (14) may be written in the alternate form

$$(14') \qquad \delta F[C] = \int_C (X\delta x + Y\delta y + Z\delta z)ds.$$

If the functional derivatives fail to exist at special points of the curve C, terms corresponding to these special points may be introduced into the formula for the variation of $F[C]$, as in the case of functionals of plane curves.

Since the true argument of the functional $F[C]$ is understood to be the curve C, and not the three functions of s which define the co-ordinates of any point of C, it follows that the three derivatives X, Y, Z are not entirely independent. In fact, if we make δx, δy, δz such that at every point of the curve they define a direction tangent to it, we have

$$\int_C (X\delta x + Y\delta y + Z\delta z)ds = 0$$

or

$$\int_C K(X \cos x, s + Y \cos y, s + Z \cos z, s)ds = 0,$$

where K is an arbitrary function of s. Hence

(15) $$X \cos x, s + Y \cos y, s + Z \cos z, s = 0.$$

According to the formulæ (14) or (14′), the derivative of $F[C]$ in any direction n is the projection R_n of the vector R, with components X, Y, Z, in that direction. Hence for new axes x', y', z' through the point, we have the usual formulæ for transformation of co-ordinates:

(16) $$X' = X \cos x, x' + Y \cos y, x' + Z \cos z, x', \text{ etc.}$$

From (15) we see moreover that the vector $R[C \,|\, M]$ is normal to the curve C at M.

The vector R has the advantage that it is uniquely defined for every point of the curve C for a given functional. It is not, however, the only functional vector which may be defined, and for additive functionals, especially, not the most convenient one.

Consider a curve C, and two planes at right angles which contain the tangent line to C at a point M. Let V_1 and V_2 be defined as

(17) $$V_1 = \lim_{\sigma_1=0} \frac{\Delta F}{\sigma_1}, \qquad V_2 = \lim_{\sigma_2=0} \frac{\Delta F}{\sigma_2},$$

due respectively to small displacements of area σ_1 and σ_2, of an element ds of the curve, in the two planes. Consider each V_i as directed normally to its plane in such a way as to make the direction around σ_i positive, looking down this normal. Let V be the vector perpendicular to C whose components are V_1 and V_2.

If $V[C \mid M]$ is continuous in C and M in the neighborhood of the point and curve in question, we can deduce in the same way as for the corresponding theorem about directional derivatives in the differential calculus, that the rate of change of $F[C]$ for a displacement σ in any plane containing the curve is the component of V perpendicular to that plane.

From the fact that, except for infinitesimals of higher order, we have the equation:

$$\Delta F = V_n d\sigma = (X\delta x + Y\delta y + Z\delta z)ds$$

we may deduce the equations

(18)
$$X = V_z \cos s, y - V_y \cos s, z,$$
$$Y = V_x \cos s, z - V_z \cos s, x,$$
$$Z = V_y \cos s, x - V_x \cos s, y,$$

which may be expressed in the shorter form

(18′)
$$R = \tau \times V,$$

where τ is a unit vector in the direction of the curve, and $\tau \times V$ stands for the vector product of the two vectors τ and V (the vector area of the parallelogram of which they are the two sides). In fact if the element of arc ds has an arbitrary vector displacement $\delta\rho$ we shall have

$$d\sigma = (\delta\rho \times \tau)ds$$

and

$$\Delta F = V \cdot d\sigma = V \cdot (\delta\rho \times \tau)ds,$$

where $V \cdot d\sigma$ stands for the scalar product of the vectors V and $d\sigma$.* But $V \cdot (\delta\rho \times \tau) = \delta\rho \cdot (\tau \times V)$, and therefore, since

---

* If α and β are two vectors, $\alpha \cdot \beta$ is defined as $\alpha_x\beta_x + \alpha_y\beta_y + \alpha_z\beta_z$. The quantity $\alpha \cdot (\beta \times \gamma)$ is thus seen to be the volume of the parallelopiped of

$V \cdot d\sigma = R \cdot \delta\rho ds$, $R = \tau \times V$. We may therefore rewrite equation (7) in the form

$$(19) \qquad F[C_2] - F[C_1] = \int\int V_n d\sigma = \int\int V \cdot d\sigma.$$

If we change V by adding to it any component in the direction τ of the curve C at M, the rate of change of $F[C]$, for a small variation about M in a plane containing the direction of the curve, will still be given by the projection of V in a direction perpendicular to this plane. *The formulæ* (18), (18'), (19) *will all remain valid,* since the terms due to this extra component all are seen to have the value zero. We can regard the functional vector $V[C \,|\, M]$ therefore as containing an arbitrary component along the curve C; in contradistinction to the vector $R[C \,|\, M]$, which is uniquely determined.

Following P. Lévy, we call $V[C \,|\, M]$ the *flux of the functional.*

9. Additive Functionals of Curves in Space. We can speak of additive functionals of curves in space, as well as additive functionals of plane curves. For additive functionals of space curves, the *flux* V acquires special importance. *We can so choose V as to make it independent of C:*

$$(20) \qquad V[C \,|\, M] = V(M) = V(xyz).$$

In fact, we notice that $V_n[C \,|\, M]$, the component of V perpendicular to the element of surface σ at M, depends merely on the orientation and position of σ, and not on the curve C, of which it forms the local variation; for, since F is additive, we have

$$(20') \qquad V_n = \lim_{\sigma=0} \frac{F[C_\sigma]}{\sigma},$$

where C_σ is the boundary of σ. Moreover, if at a point M we determine the quantities V_x, V_y, V_z in this way, by taking σ perpendicular to the x, y, and z directions respectively, the

sides α, β, γ, taken with the positive or negative sign according as the vectors have the same order as the axes, or the opposite. If we denote this triple product by $[\alpha\beta\gamma]$, we have obviously

$$[\alpha\beta\gamma] = \alpha \cdot (\beta \times \gamma) = (\alpha \times \beta) \cdot \gamma = [\beta\gamma\alpha] = [\gamma\alpha\beta].$$

construction familiar in the case of hydrodynamics shows us that V_n is merely the component in the direction N of the vector (V_x, V_y, V_z).

On account of (20'), Volterra uses the symbols $\partial F/\partial(yz)$, $\partial F/\partial(zx)$, $\partial F/\partial(xy)$ to denote the three components of V, and the symbol $dF/d\sigma$ to denote the vector V itself.

10. The Condition of Integrability for Additive Functionals.
For any closed surface we must have the equation

$$(21) \qquad \int\!\int V_n d\sigma = 0,$$

since it may be regarded as forming a double cap for a closed curve lying on it. Hence at every point in the region we are considering, the relation

$$(21') \qquad \frac{\partial V_x}{\partial x} + \frac{\partial V_y}{\partial y} + \frac{\partial V_z}{\partial z} = 0$$

must hold; *the divergence of V must everywhere vanish.*

On the other hand, it is evident, that if the relation (21') holds everywhere for the vector point function V, it will define an additive functional of space curves by (19), of which V will be the vector flux. Equation (21) will hold in fact for any closed surface, and V will satisfy (20').

11. Change of Variable.
If we make a one-one point transformation of space $x = x(\bar x \bar y \bar z)$, $y = y(\bar x \bar y \bar z)$, $z = z(\bar x \bar y \bar z)$, where $x(\bar x \bar y \bar z)$, $y(\bar x \bar y \bar z)$, $z(\bar x \bar y \bar z)$ are continuous functions with continuous first derivatives, with $[\partial(xyz)/\partial(\bar x \bar y \bar z)] \neq 0$, the closed curve C will go over into a closed curve $\bar C$, and the additive functional $F[C]$ will go over into an additive functional $\overline{F}[\overline{C}]$, which will have a flux vector $\overline{V}$.

If (u, v) are the curvilinear co-ordinates of corresponding points on the caps Σ and $\overline{\Sigma}$ of C and $\overline{C}$ respectively, then

$$\overline{F}[\overline{C}] = F[C] = \int\!\int V_x dydz + V_y dzdx + V_z dxdy$$

$$= \int\!\int \left\{ V_x \frac{\partial(yz)}{\partial(uv)} + V_y \frac{\partial(zx)}{\partial(uv)} + V_z \frac{\partial(xy)}{\partial(uv)} \right\} dudv.$$

But

$$\frac{\partial(yz)}{\partial(uv)} = \frac{\partial(yz)}{\partial(\bar{y}\bar{z})}\frac{\partial(\bar{y}\bar{z})}{\partial(uv)} + \frac{\partial(yz)}{\partial(\bar{z}\bar{x})}\frac{\partial(\bar{z}\bar{x})}{\partial(uv)} + \frac{\partial(yz)}{\partial(\bar{x}\bar{y})}\frac{\partial(\bar{x}\bar{y})}{\partial(uv)}, \text{ etc.}$$

Hence if we write

$$\overline{V}_{\bar{x}} = V_x\frac{\partial(yz)}{\partial(\bar{y}\bar{z})} + V_y\frac{\partial(zx)}{\partial(\bar{y}\bar{z})} + V_z\frac{\partial(xy)}{\partial(\bar{y}\bar{z})},$$

$$(22) \qquad \overline{V}_{\bar{y}} = V_x\frac{\partial(yz)}{\partial(\bar{z}\bar{x})} + V_y\frac{\partial(zx)}{\partial(\bar{z}\bar{x})} + V_z\frac{\partial(xy)}{\partial(\bar{z}\bar{x})},$$

$$\overline{V}_{\bar{z}} = V_x\frac{\partial(yz)}{\partial(\bar{x}\bar{y})} + V_y\frac{\partial(zx)}{\partial(\bar{x}\bar{y})} + V_z\frac{\partial(xy)}{\partial(\bar{x}\bar{y})},$$

we obtain, by substitution in the equation for $\overline{F}[\overline{C}]$, the equations

$$\overline{F}[\overline{C}] = \int\int\left\{ \overline{V}_{\bar{x}}\frac{\partial(\bar{y}\bar{z})}{\partial(uv)} + \overline{V}_{\bar{y}}\frac{\partial(\bar{z}\bar{x})}{\partial(uv)} + \overline{V}_{\bar{z}}\frac{\partial(\bar{x}\bar{y})}{\partial(uv)} \right\} dudv$$

$$= \int\int \overline{V}_{\bar{x}}d\bar{y}d\bar{z} + \overline{V}_{\bar{y}}d\bar{z}d\bar{x} + \overline{V}_{\bar{z}}d\bar{x}d\bar{y}.$$

Hence the vector whose components are defined by (22) is the transformation of V, that is, the vector flux of $F[C]$ in the new space.

If the functional $F[C]$ is not additive, the formulæ of transformation will be best given for the functional derivatives $X[C \mid M]$, $Y[C \mid M]$, $Z[C \mid M]$; since the vector flux is not uniquely defined. We have at once:

$$(23) \quad \overline{X}[\overline{C} \mid \overline{M}] = \left\{ X[C \mid M]\frac{\partial x}{\partial \bar{x}} + Y[C \mid M]\frac{\partial y}{\partial \bar{x}} + Z[C \mid M]\frac{\partial z}{\partial \bar{x}} \right\}\frac{ds}{d\bar{s}}, \text{ etc.,}$$

where ds and $d\bar{s}$ are corresponding elements of arc.

12. Functionals of Surfaces and Hypersurfaces. The main elements of the theory of functionals have been generalized by Volterra to apply to functionals of r-spaces which are immersed in an n-space, mostly for the purpose of an extension to the field of complex functionals.

The theory of functionals of hyperspaces of $n - 2$ dimensions in the n-space corresponds closely to that of functionals of curves in three dimensions. Still simpler, of course, is the theory of functionals of hyperspaces of dimension $n - 1$, except for the consideration of the singular manifolds for the functional.

Fischer* has considered the exceptional points and curves of functionals of surfaces in ordinary space, and connected his results, by examples, with the calculus of variations.

§ 3. VARIATIONAL EQUATIONS IN FUNCTIONALS OF PLANE CURVES

13. The Dependence of the Green's Function on the Boundary. The Green's function for Laplace's equation in two dimensions, denoted by $g[C \,|\, P, B]$ or $g[C \,|\, xy, x_B y_B]$, is, except for the point B, single valued and harmonic in P within the closed curve C, becomes logarithmically infinite as P approaches B:

$$g = \log \frac{1}{r} + \omega$$

and vanishes if P is on C. As is well known, it is symmetrical:

$$g[C \,|\, PB] = g[C \,|\, BP].$$

We wish to consider it now as a functional of the curve C, and express its dependence upon C.

If we take two curves C and C', the latter supposed momentarily to be entirely inside the former, and two points A and B, both inside C', which we surround with small circles, an application of Green's theorem to the complete boundary of the region between the circles and the curve C' yields the result †

$$2\pi(g[C' \,|\, AB] - g[C \,|\, AB]) = - \int_{C'} g[C \,|\, AM] \frac{\partial g[C' \,|\, MB]}{\partial n} ds,$$

upon shrinking the circles down to zero. Here n denotes the interior normal, and M a point on C corresponding to the variable of integration.

But for a small variation in C of amount $\delta n(M)$ the function $g[C \,|\, AM]$ is an infinitesimal whose principal part is $(\partial g/\partial n)\delta n$. We have therefore, upon substitution, the result:

$$(24) \quad \delta g[C \,|\, AB] = - \frac{1}{2\pi} \int_{C} \frac{\partial g[C \,|\, AM]}{\partial n} \frac{\partial g[C \,|\, MB]}{\partial n} \delta n(M) ds.$$

---

* Fischer, *American Journal of Mathematics*, vol. 38 (1916), p. 259.
† Omitted is the term

$$\int_{C'} g[C' \,|\, MB] \frac{\partial g[C \,|\, AM]}{\partial n} \delta n(M) ds$$

because it vanishes for M on C'.

Since any variation of C can be written as one which is wholly internal plus one which is wholly external, the above formula (24) applies to any variation $\delta n(M)$, continuous with continuous derivative.   It was first given by Hadamard.*

The equation (24) is called an *equation in functional derivatives*; in fact, by means of (5), it may be written in the form:

$$(24') \qquad g'[C\,|\,ABM] = -\frac{1}{2\pi}\frac{\partial g[C\,|\,AM]}{\partial n}\frac{\partial g[C\,|\,MB]}{\partial n},$$

in which $g'[C\,|\,ABM]$ denotes the functional derivative of $g[C\,|\,AB]$ at M.   It may also be called, more shortly, a *variational equation*.

If we take a family of curves of which one and only one curve passes through each point of the region, and denote by n_A and n_B the normals to the curves at A and B respectively, it follows at once, as was pointed out by Hadamard, that the quantity

$$\Phi[C\,|\,AB] = -\frac{1}{2\pi}\frac{\partial^2 g[C\,|\,AB]}{\partial n_A \partial n_B}$$

satisfies the important equation

$$(25) \qquad \delta\Phi[C\,|\,AB] = \int_C \Phi[C\,|\,AM]\Phi[C\,|\,MB]\delta n(M)ds$$

or, as it may be written,

$$(25') \qquad \Phi'[C\,|\,ABM] = \Phi[C\,|\,AM]\Phi[C\,|\,MB].$$

Hadamard's equation is also satisfied by other important differential parameters.

P. Lévy has constructed an extensive theory of these equations. They may be considered as the limits of total differential equations as the number of independent variables is allowed to become infinite.   In fact, if in the equation

$$dz = \sum_1^n f_i(x_1\cdots x_n, z)dx_i$$

we take

$$x_i = x(t_i), \qquad dx_i = \delta x(t_i)\Delta t,$$

where $\Delta t = t_{i+1} - t_i = (b-a)/n$, and write

$$f_i(x_1\cdots x_n, z) = f(x(t_1), x(t_2), \cdots, x(t_n); z\,|\,t_i)$$

letting then n become infinite, the quantity $z(x_1\cdots x_n)$ becomes

* *Comptes Rendus*, vol. 136 (1903), p. 353.

$z[\underset{a}{\overset{b}{x(t)}}]$, and we obtain the equation

$$dz = \delta z[\underset{a}{\overset{b}{x(t)}}] = \int_a^b f[x(t),\, z\,|\,t]\delta x(t)dt,$$

or

$$z'[x(t)\,|\,M] = f[\underset{a}{\overset{b}{x(t)}},\, z\,|\,M],$$

in which $z'[x(t)\,|\,M]$ denotes the functional derivative of z.

In the total differential equation there are certain *conditions of integrability* on the f_i which must be satisfied in order to make the f_i possible partial derivatives of some function $z(x_1 \cdots x_n)$. Similar conditions must therefore be expected for these new equations. Their nature can be best described in terms of an additional concept.

14. Adjoint Linear Functionals. Consider a closed curve C and let $E_1[u\,|\,M]$ and $E_2[v\,|\,M]$ be two linear functionals* of the functional arguments u and v, defined on C; functionals which depend also on the point argument M, on C. The functionals E_1 and E_2 will be said to be *adjoint* (with respect to M or s) if for every pair of functions $u(M)$, $v(M)$ in the field considered the relation

$$(26) \qquad \int_C v(M)E_1[u\,|\,M]ds = \int_C u(M)E_2[v\,|\,M]ds$$

is satisfied. The field of functions u, v will be that of all continuous functions, or continuous with their first k derivatives, as the conditions of the problem demand. It follows from (26) that the linear functionals must be homogeneous (i. e., $E[0\,|\,M] \equiv 0$) if they are to have adjoints.

From (26) it follows immediately that no linear functional admits more than one adjoint. If, in particular, $E_1[u\,|\,M]$ is merely a differential expression in u with regard to the variable s, on the curve, the equation (26) yields the well-known relations between the coefficients of the given and adjoint expressions.†

* $E[u]$ is a linear functional if $E[c_1u_1 + c_2u_2] = c_1E[u_1] + c_2E[u_2]$, where c_1 and c_2 are arbitrary constants.

† If C is not a closed curve there will be involved relations among the end values of u and its derivatives.

If our expression is of the form

$$(27) \quad E_1[u\,|\,s] = \int_C f(ss_1)u(s_1)ds_1 + A_0(s)u(s) + \sum_{i=1}^{p} A_i(s)\frac{d^iu(s)}{ds^i},$$

where s and s_1 replace M and M_1, the adjoint expression has the form

$$(27') \quad \begin{aligned} E_2[v\,|\,s] &= \int_C f(s_1s)v(s_1)ds_1 + A_0(s)v(s) \\ &\qquad + \sum_{i=1}^{p} (-1)^i \frac{d^i}{ds^i}\,(A_i(s)v(s)). \end{aligned}$$

If $E_1[u\,|\,s]$ and $F_1[u\,|\,s]$ have for adjoints $E_2[v\,|\,s]$ and $F_2[v\,|\,s]$ respectively, then $E_1[F_1[u]]$ (that is, $E_1[F_1[u\,|\,s']\,|\,s]$) has for adjoint $F_2[E_2[v]]$ (that is, $F_2[E_2[v\,|\,s']\,|\,s]$). In fact, by (26),

$$\int_C v(s)E_1[F_1[u\,|\,s']\,|\,s]ds = \int_C F_1[u\,|\,s]E_2[v\,|\,s]ds$$

$$= \int_C F_2[E_2[v\,|\,s']\,|\,s]u(s)ds.$$

Similarly, more than two expressions can be compounded, and $G_2[F_2\{E_2[v]\}]$ shown to be the adjoint of $E_1[F_1\{G_1[u]\}]$. In particular, if $E[u\,|\,M]$ is self adjoint, and F_2 is the adjoint of F_1, then the expression $F_1[E\{F_2[u]\}]$ is also self adjoint. This fact we shall make use of, later.

15. The Conditions of Integrability.

We wish to find the functional $\Phi[C\,|\,A, B \cdots]$ which will satisfy an equation of the type

$$(28) \quad \delta\Phi[C\,|\,AB\cdots] = \int_C F[C, \Phi\,|\,A, B \cdots M]\delta n(M)ds,$$

where F depends upon C and perhaps also Φ, as functional arguments (i. e., for instance upon all the values of Φ when $A, B, \cdots$ range independently over the curve C^*), and on M as a point argument. According to (28) we should expect that given $\Phi[C_0\,|\,AB\cdots]$ the functional Φ would be determined for all other curves C. This existence theorem will be considered later;

---

* In (25) F depends upon the particular values of Φ when A and B take the position M on C.

we must insure now however that Φ shall be really a functional of C, and not depend on the manner in which C is approached by the summing of successive variations from C_0.

Let $C_{\lambda\mu}$ be any two parameter family of curves containing C_0 and C, in such a way, say, that $C_{00} = C_0$, and $C_{11} = C$. In order that Φ shall not be dependent on the path that $(\lambda\mu)$ traces in going from $(0, 0)$ to $(1, 1)$ it is necessary and sufficient that

$$\frac{\partial}{\partial\mu}\frac{\partial\Phi}{\partial\lambda} = \frac{\partial}{\partial\lambda}\frac{\partial\Phi}{\partial\mu}.$$

This condition must hold for every two parameter family which can be formed from the class of curves we are considering.

If we write $\delta^2 = \delta(\delta\Phi)$, we shall have for it the value

$$\frac{\partial^2\Phi}{\partial\lambda\partial\mu}\, d\lambda d\mu$$

and the test for integrability, corresponding to the possibility of interchanging the order of differentiation in regard to λ and μ, lies in the possibility of interchanging the two variations δn and $\delta_1 n$ of C without changing $\delta^2\Phi$.

The variation of $\delta\Phi$, as given by (28), due to the new variation $\delta_1 n(M_1)$, depends upon the variation of F, which we may write as some linear functional $E[\delta_1 n \,|\, M]$ of $\delta_1 n$, upon the variation of δn itself (i. e., $\partial/\partial\mu(\partial n/\partial\lambda)d\lambda d\mu$), which we call $\delta^2 n$, and on the variation of ds. The last is obviously given by the formula

$$- k\delta_1 n\delta s,$$

where k is the curvature, counted positively if the center of curvature lies on the positive direction of n. We have, then:

$$(29) \quad \delta^2\Phi = \int_C E[\delta_1 n \,|\, M]\delta n(M)ds$$
$$+ \int_C F[C, \Phi \,|\, M](\delta^2 n - k\delta n\delta_1 n)ds.$$

In order to investigate more closely the quantity $\delta^2 n$ consider the special equation

$$\Psi[C] = \iint\limits_{(C)} f(M)dxdy,$$

which defines Ψ as a functional of curves. We have

$$\delta\Psi[C] = \int_C f(M)\delta n ds$$

and

$$\delta^2\Psi[C] = \int_C \frac{\partial f}{\partial n}\delta_1 n \delta n ds + \int_C f(M)(\delta^2 n - k\delta n \delta_1 n)ds,$$

provided that we define (as a permanent convention) the path of the point M as normal to C, as C varies. But in this equation $\delta^2\Psi$ is independent of the order of making the variations δn, $\delta_1 n$, since Ψ is a functional of C; also, obviously, are the first and third terms of the right-hand member. Hence the same property holds for $\int_C f(M)\delta^2 n ds$, whatever the function $f(M)$ may be. *Hence $\delta^2 n$ itself is independent of the order of making the variations δn and $\delta_1 n$.*

With reference to the original equation (29) therefore, we see that the necessary and sufficient condition for integrability is that the functional $E[\delta_1 n \,|\, M]$ be self adjoint. But this functional is merely the variation of $\Phi'[C \,|\, AB \cdots M]$. Hence *the necessary and sufficient condition for the integrability of* (28) *is that*

$$\delta\Phi'[C \,|\, AB \cdots M]$$

be a self adjoint functional of δn.

If $E[\delta n \,|\, M]$ is identically self adjoint, that is, for every Φ and C, the equation (28) is said to be *completely integrable.*

In calculating the functional E we must not expect to find it in the simple form (5), since the variation of the point M with C as C varies is usually going to introduce new terms into the expression.

16. Special Equations. In the case of Hadamard's equation, we have

$$\delta\Phi'[C \,|\, ABM] = \Phi[C \,|\, AM]\delta\Phi[C \,|\, MB] + \delta\Phi[C \,|\, AM]\Phi[C \,|\, MB]$$

$$= \int_C \{\Phi[C \,|\, AM]\Phi[C \,|\, MM_1]\Phi[C \,|\, M_1 B]$$

$$+ \Phi[C \,|\, AM_1]\Phi[C \,|\, M_1 M]\Phi[C \,|\, MB]\}\delta_1 n(M_1)ds_1$$

$$+ \frac{\partial}{\partial n}\{\Phi[C \,|\, AM]\Phi[C \,|\, MB]\}\delta_1 n(M).$$

As a functional of $\delta_1 n$, this expression, according to (27), is its own adjoint; for the integral is symmetrical in M and M_1, and the term outside the integral is merely of the form of a function of M multiplied into $\delta_1 n(M)$. *Hadamard's equation is therefore completely integrable.*

On the other hand, the condition of integrability for the somewhat similar equation

$$(30) \qquad \Phi'[C\,|\,ABM] = \Phi[C\,|\,AM]\Phi[C\,|\,BM]$$

reduces by (27) to the condition:

$$\Phi(AM)\Phi(MM_1)\Phi(BM_1) + \Phi(AM_1)\Phi(MM_1)\Phi(BM)$$
$$= \Phi(AM_1)\Phi(M_1M)\Phi(BM) + \Phi(AM)\Phi(M_1M)\Phi(BM_1)$$

or

$$(30') \qquad \{\Phi(AM)\Phi(BM_1) \dotplus \Phi(AM_1)\Phi(BM)\}\{\Phi(MM_1) - \Phi(M_1M)\} = 0.$$

In these equations the C is omitted for brevity; it must be remembered that the points M and M_1 are however restricted to lying on the curve C.

If the first factor of (30') is identically zero, we find $\Phi[C\,|\,AM] \equiv 0$, by putting $B = A$. Hence by (30), $\Phi'[C\,|\,ABM]$ vanishes identically, and therefore, by (7),

$$\Phi[C\,|\,AB] \equiv \text{const.} \equiv 0.$$

If on the other hand, the second factor vanishes identically (which is the alternative if we restrict ourselves to functionals Φ which are analytic in their point arguments) we have

$$\Phi[C_0\,|\,AB] = \Phi[C_0\,|\,BA]$$

provided that C_0 goes through both A and B. But since from (30), for every C, A, B,

$$\Phi'[C\,|\,ABM] \equiv \Phi'[C\,|\,BAM],$$

it follows by (7) that the function $\Phi[C\,|\,AB] - \Phi[C\,|\,BA]$ is independent of the curve C. Hence, identically:

$$\Phi[C\,|\,AB] = \Phi[C\,|\,BA],$$

which is a sufficient condition for integrability.

Consider as a third equation

$$\delta\Phi[C] = \int_C f(\Phi, M)\delta n(M)ds, \tag{31}$$

for which we have

$$\delta\Phi'[C\,|\,M] = \frac{\partial f(\Phi, M)}{\partial\Phi}\,\delta\Phi + \frac{\partial f(\Phi, M)}{\partial n}\,\delta_1 n(M)$$

$$= \int_C \frac{\partial f(\Phi, M)}{\partial\Phi}\,f(\Phi, m_1)\delta_1 n(M_1)ds_1 + \frac{\partial f(\Phi, M)}{\partial n}\,\delta_1 n(M).$$

By (27) the condition of integrability is the following:

$$\frac{\partial f(\Phi, M)}{\partial\Phi}f(\Phi, M_1) = \frac{\partial f(\Phi, M_1)}{\partial\Phi}f(\Phi, M). \tag{31'}$$

If the equation is to be completely integrable, this condition must be satisfied for all functionals Φ and points M and M_1 on C. This is the same as saying that $\partial \log f(\Phi M)/\partial\Phi$ shall be independent of M, M on C. Hence, for M on C, f must be of the form:

$$f(\Phi, M) = g(\Phi)\varphi(M),$$

and since the function does not involve C it must have this form always. Therefore, by (30)

$$\frac{\delta\Phi}{g(\Phi)} = \int_C \varphi(M)\delta nds.$$

The right-hand member of this equation is merely $\delta\Psi[C]$, where

$$\Psi[C] = \iint\limits_{(C)} \varphi(M)d\sigma$$

is an arbitrary additive functional. But the relation

$$\delta\Phi/g(\Phi) = \delta\Psi$$

merely tells us that the quantities Φ and Ψ are functionally dependent, i. e., that $d\Phi/d\Psi$ exists and is given by $g(\Phi)$. Hence *the functionals defined by* (30), *if* (30) *is completely integrable, are merely functions of additive functionals of curves C.*

As a last example, consider the equation

$$\delta\Phi[C] = \int_C \Phi'[C\,|\,M]\delta n(M)ds,$$

which is an identity for any given functional $\Phi[C]$, under the conditions described for (7). Let us suppose that $\Phi'[C\,|\,M]$ has itself an integrable derivative $\Phi''[C\,|\,MM_1]$. We shall have then for $\delta\Phi'$ the expression

$$\int_C \Phi''[C\,|\,MM_1]\delta_1 n(M_1)ds,$$

plus possibly other terms which are not integrals. The condition

$$\Phi''[C\,|\,MM_1] = \Phi''[C\,|\,M_1M]$$

must therefore be included in the condition of integrability, a result which was originally stated by Volterra. *The second functional derivative must be symmetrical in its point arguments.*

17. The Integrability of the Equation for the Green's Function. For the equation

$$(32) \qquad \Phi'[C\,|\,ABM] = -\frac{\partial\Phi[C\,|\,AM]}{\partial n}\frac{\partial\Phi[C\,|\,MB]}{\partial n},$$

which is equivalent except for a constant to (24'), we have

$$\begin{aligned}
\delta\Phi'(ABM) = -\int &\Bigg[\frac{\partial\Phi(AM)}{\partial n}\frac{\partial\Phi(M_1B)}{\partial n_1}\frac{\partial^2\Phi(MM_1)}{\partial n\partial n_1} \\
&+ \frac{\partial\Phi(AM_1)}{\partial n_1}\frac{\partial\Phi(MB)}{\partial n}\frac{\partial^2\Phi(M_1M)}{\partial n\partial n_1} \Bigg]\delta_1 n(s_1)ds_1 \\
&- \frac{\partial}{\partial n}\left(\frac{\partial\Phi(AM)}{\partial n}\frac{\partial\Phi(MB)}{\partial n}\right)\delta_1 n(s) \\
&+ \left(\frac{\partial\Phi(AM)}{\partial s}\frac{\partial\Phi(MB)}{\partial n} + \frac{\partial\Phi(MB)}{\partial s}\frac{\partial\Phi(AM)}{\partial n}\right)\delta_1 n'(s),
\end{aligned}$$

in which the last two terms represent the variation of the right-hand member of (32) due to the displacement of the point M, the last term arising from the change of direction of n. The notation $\delta_1 n'(s)$ stands for the derivative with respect to s of the quantity $\delta_1 n$.

In order for this expression to be self adjoint, we have, by (27):

$$(33) \qquad \frac{\partial\Phi(AM)}{\partial s}\frac{\partial\Phi(MB)}{\partial n} + \frac{\partial\Phi(MB)}{\partial s}\frac{\partial\Phi(AM)}{\partial n} = 0$$

for all curves C, all points A and B, and all points M on C. *Equation (32) is therefore not completely integrable.* Since (30) is an identity, its variation also must vanish. This will be constituted by an integral, a term in δn and a term in $\delta n'$. By choosing particular types of functions $\delta n(s)$ it is easily seen that each of these terms must vanish separately.

The coefficient of $\delta n'$ is called by Lévy the *derivative with respect to* $\delta n'$. Thus the derivative with respect to $\delta n'$ of $\partial \Phi(AM)/\partial n$ is $-\partial \Phi(AM)/\partial s$, and the derivative of $\partial \Phi(AM)/\partial s$ is $+\partial \Phi(AM)/\partial n$. Hence we can write down at once the derivative with respect to $\delta n'$ of the left-hand member of (33), and since this must vanish, we have the further identity

$$(33') \qquad \frac{\partial \Phi(AM)}{\partial n}\frac{\partial \Phi(MB)}{\partial n} - \frac{\partial \Phi(AM)}{\partial s}\frac{\partial \Phi(MB)}{\partial s} = 0.$$

Consider functionals Φ which as far as concerns the point arguments, are continuous with continuous derivatives in the neighborhood of the curve C. It can be shown quite simply that this requires either (a), that Φ shall be independent of C and shall be a function merely of a single point argument A or B, or (b), that if it depends upon C, it shall, as far as its point arguments are concerned, be an analytic function of $x + iy$ and $x_1 - iy_1$, where $A = (xy)$, $B = (x_1 y_1)$, and $i = \pm \sqrt{-1}$. In fact, in this last case, from the equations (33), (33') follow the equations:

$$\frac{\partial \Phi(AM)}{\partial n} = i\frac{\partial \Phi(AM)}{\partial s}, \qquad \frac{\partial \Phi(MB)}{\partial n} = -i\frac{\partial \Phi(MB)}{\partial s},$$

from which the above conclusion can be shown to follow.

The value of the functional may be chosen arbitrarily for one curve C_0, and is then determined by the equation for the other curves C.

The Green's function does not remain continuous when A and B approach the same point M on the curve, and hence is not subject to the above analysis. Lévy has the following theorem:

Consider a functional $\Phi[C \mid AB]$, *equal to the function* $(1/2\pi)g[C \mid AB]$ *plus a function which remains analytic when the point arguments lie in the neighborhood of the curve. A necessary and sufficient condition that there exist such a functional which satisfies* (32) *and takes on, for a given curve* C_0 *given arbitrary values* $\Phi_0[C \mid AB]$, *is that*

$$(33') \qquad \frac{\partial \Phi_0(AM)}{\partial s} = \frac{\partial \Phi_0(MB)}{\partial s} = 0;$$

that is, that Φ_0 *shall remain constant if one point argument is held fast and the other allowed to travel around the curve* C_0.

18. Variational vs. Integro-Differential Equations. If equation (28) is completely integrable, we can obtain its solution by means of any particular family of curves we please, which leads to the curve C. In this way, by introducing a quantity λ as a parameter which determines the curve of the family, the equation under consideration becomes an integro-differential equation, or perhaps reduces to a degenerate form of such an equation.

Consider the equation

$$(34) \qquad \delta \Phi[C] = \int_C F[C \mid \Phi, M]\delta n(M)ds,$$

in which the functional $\Phi[C]$ has no point arguments. If we introduce a second parameter t for the set of orthogonal trajectories to the λ-curves, we may write $\delta n(M)ds = r(\lambda t)d\lambda dt$, where $r(\lambda t)$ is a known function, so that (34) takes the form

(34') $$\frac{d\Phi}{d\lambda} = \int_{T_0}^{T_1} F(\lambda, \Phi, t)r(\lambda t)dt.$$

This equation may reduce to a differential equation; in any case, however, if we integrate with respect to λ from λ_0 to λ we have an implicit functional equation of the type which is described in Art. 36, Lecture III. Hence the theorem: *Within a certain range R of the xy plane, and a range of values $\Phi_0 - L$* $\leq \Phi \leq \Phi_0 + L$, *there is one and only one continuous solution $\Phi[C]$ of (34), for C in R, which takes on the value Φ_0 for the curve C_0; provided that $F[C \,|\, \Phi, M]$ is continuous in its three arguments, and there is a constant A (independent of C and M) such that:*

(34'') $$| F[C \,|\, \Phi_2, M] - F[C \,|\, \Phi_1, M] | \leq A \,|\Phi_2 - \Phi_1|\,.$$

If we consider the more general equation (28) we must replace the point arguments A, B, $\cdots$ by their curvilinear co-ordinates $(\lambda_1 t_1)$, $(\lambda_2 t_2)$, $\cdots$. If the functional F, which now depends upon all the values of Φ, for t_1, t_2, $\cdots$ moving independently over their common range, satisfies still a Cauchy-Lipschitz condition of the type (34''), the treatment of the equation depends merely upon the same theorem about implicit functional equations. If on the other hand, the functional F depends upon Φ in such a way as to bring in its derivatives with respect to one or more of the arguments, the theory of the equation must be a generalization of the theory of partial differential equations. The two equations (25) and (32), respectively, offer examples of these two types.

§ 4. PARTIAL VARIATIONAL EQUATIONS

19. Volterra's Equation for the Dirichlet Integral. Upon the convention that we have already made, that as C varies, the point M is understood to move in the direction of the normal to C at M, we shall speak of a functional $u[C \,|\, M]$ as being independent of C if it remains invariant as M changes with C. We are thus able to consider functionals Φ which depend upon a curve C and a function $u(M)$ on the curve C, each varying independently of the other; and we can consider the partial functional derivatives of such functionals with respect to C and u, and the possible relations that may hold between them.

Dirichlet's integral

(35) $$\Phi[C, u] = \int\int_{(C)} \left\{ \left(\frac{\partial u}{\partial x}\right)^2 + \left(\frac{\partial u}{\partial y}\right)^2 \right\} dxdy,$$

where $u(x, y)$ is a solution of Laplace's equation inside C, is a functional of the contour C and the values $u(M)$ which are assigned to $u(x, y)$ on C. If we change $u(M)$ without changing C, we have:

$$\delta_u \Phi = 2 \int\int_{(C)} \left\{ \frac{\partial u}{\partial x} \delta \frac{\partial u}{\partial x} + \frac{\partial u}{\partial y} \delta \frac{\partial u}{\partial y} \right\} dxdy$$

which reduces by an integration by parts and the setting of $\nabla^2 u = 0$, to the form

$$\delta_u \Phi = -2 \int_C \frac{\partial \dot{u}}{\partial n} \delta u \, ds.$$

By means of the definition of functional derivative, this yields:

$$(36) \qquad \Phi_u'[C, u \mid M] = -2 \frac{\partial u(M)}{\partial n}.$$

On the other hand, if we vary C, and vary $u(M)$ on C at the same time in such a way that $u(xy)$ remains unchanged inside C, that is so that $\delta u = \partial u/\partial n \; \delta n$, we have for the new quantity

$$\delta \Phi = \int_C \{\Phi_u'(M)\delta u(M) + \Phi_C'(M)\delta n(M)\} ds$$

$$= \int_C \left\{ \Phi_u'(M) \frac{\partial u}{\partial n} + \Phi_C'(M) \right\} \delta n(M) ds$$

the formula

$$\delta \Phi = -\int_C \left\{ \left(\frac{\partial u}{\partial x}\right)^2 + \left(\frac{\partial u}{\partial y}\right)^2 \right\} \delta n \; ds$$

$$= -\int_C \left\{ \left(\frac{\partial u}{\partial n}\right)^2 + u'^2 \right\} \delta n \; ds,$$

where u' denotes $\partial u/\partial s$. Hence:

$$\Phi_u'(M) \frac{\partial u}{\partial n} + \Phi_C'(M) = -\left(\frac{\partial u}{\partial n}\right)^2 - u'^2.$$

By means of (36) this yields the equation

$$(37) \qquad \Phi_C'[C, u \mid M] = \tfrac{1}{4}\{\Phi_u'[C, u \mid M]\}^2 - \{u'(M)\}^2,$$

which is a partial equation in the functional derivatives of $\Phi[C \mid u]$ involving only the independent arguments C, and $u(M)$ on C (since $\partial u/\partial s$ is known when u is known on C).

Equations of the type (37) may be called partial variational equations, or equations in partial functional derivatives. We may expect to find them for such functionals as are related to partial differential equations by means of the Calculus of Variations; for some such connection is necessary in order to eliminate the interior values of $u(xy)$ from explicit connection with the quantities considered. Quantities like the area of minimal surfaces, the energy in a changing system, etc., will therefore satisfy such equations. In particular, to give another special example, if within the closed curve C, the quantity $u(xy)$ is a solution of the equation

$$\frac{\partial^2 u}{\partial x^2} + \frac{\partial^2 u}{\partial y^2} = \lambda u,$$

the quantity

$$\Psi[C, u] = \iint\limits_{(C)} \left\{ \left(\frac{\partial u}{\partial x}\right)^2 + \left(\frac{\partial u}{\partial y}\right)^2 + \lambda u^2 \right\} dxdy$$

satisfies the partial variational equation

$$(38) \qquad \Psi_C'[C, u \mid M] = \tfrac{1}{4}\{\Psi_u'[C, u \mid M]\}^2 - u'(M)^2 - \lambda u(M)^2.$$

20. The Condition of Integrability. The equation to be considered is of the form

$$(39) \qquad \Phi_C'[C, u \mid M] = F[C, u, \Phi_u' \mid \Phi, M].$$

We have already considered the second variation of a functional $u[C]$. of C alone. If the functional depends also on M, its second variation takes on a more complicated form. This can be arrived at in the following manner,

Consider two separate variations δn and $\delta_1 n$ depending on parameters λ and μ; the final position of a point M will be M_1 or M_2 according to which of the variations is executed first, and the corresponding difference between the values of $u[C \mid M]$ will be $M_1 M_2 \, \partial u/\partial s$. Accordingly, if $\partial u/\partial s$ vanishes identically on C, the quantity $\delta^2 u[C \mid M]$ will be independent of the order of making the variations δn and $\delta_1 n$, from that particular curve C.

Given now any functional $u[C \mid M]$ we can write it in the neighborhood of C as $u_1[C \mid M] + u_2(xy)$, taking for the first term a functional which remains constant on the particular curve C, and for the second, a function of x, y independent of the curve C. The second variation of $u_2(xy)$ will involve a differentiation with respect to $\delta n'$, according to the method of Art. 17, and we shall therefore have:

$$\delta^2 u_2 = \frac{\partial^2 u_2}{\partial n \partial n_1} \, \delta n \delta n_1 - \frac{\partial u_2}{\partial s} \, \delta_1 n' \delta n + \frac{\partial u_2}{\partial n} \, \delta^2 n,$$

and accordingly, since $\partial^2 u_2/\partial n \, \partial_1 n$ and $\delta^2 n$ are independent of the order of making δn and $\delta_1 n$, the quantity $\delta^2 u_2 + u_2' \delta_1 n' \delta n$ must be also. But the same property holds for the quantity $\delta^2 u_1 + u_1' \delta_1 n' \delta n$, and therefore we have the result that *the expression*

$$\delta^2 u + u' \delta_1 n' \delta n$$

is symmetrical in δn *and* $\delta_1 n$.

Return now to the condition of integrability for (39). The variations of Φ_C' and Φ_u' will be linear functionals of $\delta_1 n$ and $\delta_1 u$. If we write them in the form

(40)
$$\delta \Phi_u'[C, u \mid M] = E[\delta_1 u] + F[\delta_1 n] + k \Phi_u'[C, u \mid M] \delta_1 n$$
$$\delta \Phi_C'[C, u \mid M] = \bar{F}[\delta_1 u] + G[\delta_1 n] + \Phi_u'[C, u \mid M] u' \delta_1 n',$$

the last term in each expression being inserted merely for convenience, we find, in the same way as in (29), for the second variation of Φ:

(41)
$$\delta^2 \Phi[C, u] = \int_C \{ E[\delta_1 u] \delta n + F[\delta_1 n] \delta u + \bar{F}[\delta_1 u] \delta n + G[\delta_1 n] \delta n \} ds$$
$$+ \int_C \{ \Phi_u'(M)(\delta^2 u + u' \delta_1 n' \delta n) + \Phi_C'(M)(\delta^2 n - k \delta_1 n \delta n) \} ds.$$

The second integral is already independent of the order of making the successive variations. In order to produce the same result in the first integral, and therefore, *in order to make* $\delta \Phi$ *an exact differential, it is necessary and sufficient that the functionals* $E[\delta u]$ *and* $G[\delta n]$ *be self adjoint, and that the functionals* $\bar{F}[\delta u]$ *and* $F[\delta n]$ *be mutually adjoint.*

Let us apply this result to equation (39). We are assuming that $\Phi[C, u]$ is such a functional that:

$$\delta \Phi = \int_C \{ \Phi_C'[C, u \mid M] \delta n + \Phi_u'[C, u \mid M] \delta u \} ds,$$

and we may therefore substitute this value for $\delta \Phi$ when we find the variation of $\delta \Phi'$ in (39). We have then:

(42) $$\delta\Phi_C'[C, u \mid M] = H[\delta\Phi_u'] + L[\delta u] + L_1[\delta n]$$

where the functionals H, L and L_1 depend upon the arguments indicated, and on Φ, C, M, $u(M)$, $\Phi_u'[C, u \mid M]$ and the derivatives of δu and δn.

From (40) and (42) we have:

$$\delta\Phi_C'[C, u \mid M] = H[E[\delta u]] + H[F[\delta n]] + H[k\Phi_u'\delta n] + L[\delta u] + L_1[\delta n]$$

whence

$$\overline{F}[\delta u] = H[E[\delta u]] + L[\delta u]$$

$$G[\delta n] + \Phi_C'u'\delta n' = H[F[\delta n]] + H[k\Phi_u'\delta n] + L_1[\delta n].$$

Denote by $\overline{H}$ and $\overline{L}$ the adjoints respectively of H and L. If E is self adjoint and $\overline{F}$ is the adjoint of F, we must have, by Art. 14:

$$F[\delta n] = E[\overline{H}[\delta n]] + \overline{L}[\delta n]$$

and therefore

$$G[\delta n] = H[E[\overline{H}[\delta n]]] + H[\overline{L}[\delta n]] + H[k\Phi_u'\delta n] + L[\delta n] - \Phi_u'u'\delta n'.$$

Hence if $G[\delta n]$ is to be self adjoint, and thus $\delta\Phi$ an exact differential, it is necessary that the expression

(43) $$H[\overline{L}[\delta n]] + H[k\Phi_u'\delta n] + L_1[\delta n] - \Phi_u'u'\delta n'$$

be self adjoint.

If the expression (43) *is self adjoint identically, that is, for all curves C and quantities Φ, $u(M)$ and Φ_u', the equation* (39) *is said to be completely integrable.*

With reference to equation (37), we have

$$\delta\Phi_C'[C, u \mid M] = \tfrac{1}{2}\Phi_u'\delta\Phi_u' - 2u'\delta\{u'(M)\}$$
$$= \tfrac{1}{2}\Phi_u'\delta\Phi_u' - 2u'(\delta u)' - 2ku'^2\delta n$$

since

$$\delta\{u'(M)\} = \delta\frac{du}{ds} = \frac{d\delta u}{ds} - \frac{du}{ds}\frac{d\delta s}{ds} = (\delta u)' + ku'\delta n.$$

Hence

$$H[\delta\Phi_u'] = \tfrac{1}{2}\Phi_u'\delta\Phi_u',$$
$$L[\delta u] = -2u'(\delta u)',$$
$$L_1[\delta n] = -2ku'^2\delta n,$$

and from the second of these equations it follows that:

$$\overline{L}[\delta n] = 2u'\delta n' + 2u''\delta n$$

so that (43) takes the form

$$u'\Phi_u'\delta n' + u''\Phi_u'\delta n + \tfrac{1}{2}k\Phi_u'^2\delta n - 2ku'^2\delta n - u'\Phi_u'\delta n',$$

which is identically self adjoint, since the terms in $\delta n'$ annul each other. *Hence equation* (37) *is completely integrable.*

The same fact is true of equation (38).

By a process analogous to that which we have already discussed in Art. 13, in describing the generalization of a system of partial differential equations in one dependent function to a variational equation in a corresponding functional, we may (with Lévy) arrive at equations of the type of (39); only in this case we must separate the independent variables into two sets, $x_1 \cdots x_n$, corresponding to the argument u, and $y_1 \cdots y_n$, corresponding to the argument C. The related system of differential equations will then be the following:

$$(44) \qquad \frac{\partial z}{\partial y_i} = f_i \left(x_1 \cdots x_n,\, y_1 \cdots y_n,\, z,\, \frac{\partial z}{\partial x_1} \cdots \frac{\partial z}{\partial x_n} \right), \qquad i = 1, 2, \cdots, n.$$

The conditions of integrability have been deduced for (39) in the same way as the more familiar conditions are deduced for (44); in fact the condition that (43) be self adjoint is merely the analog of the relations

$$
\begin{aligned}
(45) \qquad & \frac{\partial f_i}{\partial y_j} + f_j \frac{\partial f_i}{\partial z} + \sum_{k=1}^{n} \frac{\partial f_i}{\partial p_k} \left(\frac{\partial f_j}{\partial x_k} + p_k \frac{\partial f_j}{\partial z} \right) \\
& = \frac{\partial f_j}{\partial y_i} + f_i \frac{\partial f_j}{\partial z} + \sum_{k=1}^{n} \frac{\partial f_j}{\partial p_k} \left(\frac{\partial f_i}{\partial x_k} + p_k \frac{\partial f_i}{\partial z} \right), \qquad i, j = 1, 2, \cdots, n,
\end{aligned}
$$

in which p_k stands for $\partial z / \partial x_k$.

The equation (39) and its treatment are thus seen to be the result of the same significant and fruitful process of generalization which lies at the basis of the theory of functionals and the theory of integral equations.

Fundamental problems for (44) are (a) the determination of a solution which for $y_1 = y_2 = \cdots = y_n = 0$ takes on values which are given analytic functions of $x_1 \cdots x_n$, and (b) the determination of a solution which when

$$x_i = \xi_i(y_1 \cdots y_n), \qquad i = 1, 2, \cdots, n,$$

takes on the values $z = \zeta_0(y_1 \cdots y_n)$. Their analogs in the present case are (a) the determination of a solution of (39) which for $C = C_0$ takes on assigned values $\Phi[C_0,\, u]$, and (b) the determination of a solution of (39) which reduces to assigned values $\Psi[C,\, v]$ when $u(M)$ is put equal to some function $v(M)$, given on each C (i. e., when $u(M) = v[C \mid M]$).

The theory of the second problem, as developed by Lévy, involves the solution of implicit functional equations, as treated in our Lecture III, and an extension of the concept of *characteristic*, as applied to the equations (44). This new concept seems to be necessary for any use of these equations in applied mathematics.

LECTURE II.

COMPLEX FUNCTIONALS.*

§ 1. The Relation of Isogeneity

21. Isogeneity and Complex Vector Fluxes. Our survey of the theory of functionals of curves in space, as taken up in Lecture I, cannot be complete without a study of the possible relations that may hold between them as complex quantities. This study serves to generalize some of the basic properties of analytic functions. It is not impossible that there should be more than one direction of investigation to carry out this purpose; the present theory, which is due to Volterra, has as its basis the relation of *isogeneity*, which is the generalization to functionals of curves, in space, of the relation which holds between two complex point functions on a surface, when one is an analytic function of the other. The relation between conjugate functions has, however, a different generalization (see Art. 48). In this lecture Volterra's theory is presented in terms of the linear vector function, and the analysis thus somewhat simplified.

Consider the two complex functionals $F[C] = F_1[C] + iF_2[C]$ and $\Phi[C] = \Phi_1[C] + i\Phi_2[C]$, and make a small continuous variation of C in the neighborhood of P, of area $\sigma\Sigma$, of the sort used for defining a vector flux. If the ratio of the increments of Φ and F, namely the quantity:

$$\frac{\Delta\Phi_1 + i\Delta\Phi_2}{\Delta F_1 + i\Delta F_2},$$

* This lecture is based upon the following references:

V. Volterra: Sur une généralisation de la théorie des fonctions d'une variable imaginaire, *Acta Mathematica*, vol. 12 (1889), pp. 233–286;

The generalization of analytic functions, *Book of the Opening*, Rice Institute (1917), vol. 3, pp. 1036–1084.

Poincaré, Sur les résidus des intégrales doubles, *Acta Mathematica*, vol. 9 (1887), pp. 321–384.

P. Lévy, Sur les équations intégro-differentielles définissant des fonctions de lignes, *Thèses présentées à la Faculté des Sciences de Paris*, no. d'ordre 1436.

approaches a limit, as σ approaches zero, independent of the surface on which the variation takes place, we denote the value of this limit by

$$(1) \qquad \frac{d\Phi}{dF} = \lim_{\sigma=0} \frac{\Delta\Phi_1 + i\Delta\Phi_2}{\Delta F_1 + i\Delta F_2},$$

and say that Φ is *isogenous* to F. The relation is obviously reciprocal; moreover, if two functionals are isogenous to a third they are isogenous to each other. The relation of isogeneity may be expressed in terms of the vector fluxes of F and Φ.

Denote by V_1, V_2, W_1 and W_2 the components of the vector fluxes of F_1, F_2, Φ_1 and Φ_2 respectively, normal to the curve C at the point P. Denote by W_1' and W_1'' the vector components (or their algebraic values, as the context in any particular case will determine) of W_1 in the directions V_1 and V_2 respectively; similarly for W_2. If now we make in the neighborhood of the point P two variations of the curve C, of areas σ_1 and σ_2, the first containing V_1 in its plane of variation, thus contributing nothing as an increment of F_1, and the second containing V_2 in its plane of variation and therefore not changing F_2, we obtain two expressions for $d\Phi/dF$. As a necessary condition for isogeneity these must be equal:

$$\frac{(W_1'' + iW_2'') \cdot d\sigma_1}{iV_2 \cdot d\sigma_1} = \frac{(W_1' + iW_2') \cdot d\sigma_2}{V_1 \cdot d\sigma_2},$$

or

$$(2) \qquad \frac{W_1'' + iW_2''}{i\,|V_2|} = \frac{W_1' + iW_2'}{|V_1|},$$

where $|V_1|$ and $|V_2|$ denote the absolute values of the respective vectors.

The deduction just given is no longer valid if V_1 and V_2 happen to have the same direction. But in this case W_1 and W_2 are also co-directional and have the same direction as V_1 and V_2, as we see by taking a variation which contains this vector in its plane. If, on the other hand, V_1 and V_2 are equal in magnitude and at right angles, equation (2) shows that W_1 and W_2 will be similarly related. In fact, as P. Lévy has pointed out, the equation (2) implies that if an ellipse is constructed with conjugate semidiameters V_1 and V_2, W_1 and W_2 will be conjugate semidiameters in an ellipse similar to this and similarly placed.

22. Summary of the Properties of the Linear Vector Function. For the purpose of expressing the condition (2) in convenient form, it is desirable to have at hand a few of the important formulæ for the manipulation of linear vector functions. They are for convenience summarized in this section.

A vector W is a *linear vector function* of a vector V if when $V = c_1V_1 + c_2V_2$, where c_1 and c_2 are constants, it follows that $W = c_1W_1 + c_2W_2$. The properties of this relation can be briefly and conveniently expressed in terms of the Gibbs concept of *dyadic*.

A dyadic is the sum of symbolic products of the form

$$A = \alpha_1\beta_1 + \alpha_2\beta_2 + \cdots + \alpha_k\beta_k,$$

the nature of the product being defined merely by the fact that when the dyadic is combined with a vector ρ on the right (notation $A \cdot \rho$) a new vector ρ' is produced, which is given by the equation

$$(3) \qquad \rho' = A \cdot \rho = \alpha_1(\beta_1 \cdot \rho) + \alpha_2(\beta_2 \cdot \rho) + \cdots + \alpha_k(\beta_k \cdot \rho).$$

Obviously, according to this equation, the vector ρ' is a linear vector function of the vector ρ. Two dyadics are said to be equal if they represent the same transformation, that is, if when combined right-handedly with an arbitrary ρ, the same vector ρ' in both cases is produced.

Similarly we can define multiplication on the left of a dyadic by a vector, and show that the resulting vector is uniquely determined, that is, that two equal dyadics produce the same vector by multiplication on the left, although of course generally a different vector from that produced by multiplication on the right.

The following properties of dyadics follow immediately from the definition:

(a) $$\rho' \cdot (A \cdot \rho) = (\rho' \cdot A) \cdot \rho,$$

so that the notation $\rho' \cdot A \cdot \rho$ has no ambiguity.

(b) $$\alpha(\beta + \gamma) = \alpha\beta + \alpha\gamma.$$
(c) If

$$A_1 = \alpha_1'\beta_1' + \alpha_2'\beta_2' + \cdots + \alpha_k'\beta_k',$$

$$A_2 = \alpha_1''\beta_1'' + \alpha_2''\beta_2'' + \cdots + \alpha_n''\beta_n'',$$

and A_3 is the dyadic such that $A_3 \cdot \rho = A_2 \cdot (A_1 \cdot \rho)$, then it may be expressed in the form

$$(4) \qquad A_3 = A_2 \cdot A_1 = \Sigma_{ij}\, \alpha_i''(\beta_i'' \cdot \alpha_j')\beta_j',$$

whence it is called the product of A_1 by A_2. In general $A_2 \cdot A_1$ is not the same as $A_1 \cdot A_2$.

(d) If A_3 is the dyadic such that $A_3 \cdot \rho = A_1 \cdot \rho + A_2 \cdot \rho$ it may be expressed in the form

$$A_3 = \Sigma_i\, \alpha_i'\beta_i' + \Sigma_j\, \alpha_j''\beta_j'',$$

whence it is called the sum of A_1 and A_2. Obviously:

$$A_1 + A_2 = A_2 + A_1.$$

(e) If A_c is the dyadic such that $\rho \cdot A_c = A \cdot \rho$, then A_c is called the conjugate of A, and we have for it the expression

$$(5) \qquad A_c = \Sigma_i \beta_i \alpha_i.$$

The vectors in any dyadic may be resolved into components, and the resulting products expanded according to the distributive law. If we take three unit vectors i, j, k, mutually normal, any dyadic may be expressed in the form

$$a_{11}ii + a_{12}ij + a_{13}ik + a_{21}ji + \cdots + a_{33}kk,$$

and represented by the matrix

$$\begin{pmatrix} a_{11} & a_{12} & a_{13} \\ a_{21} & a_{22} & a_{23} \\ a_{31} & a_{32} & a_{33} \end{pmatrix}.$$

The multiplication of dyadics is, as we have seen, equivalent to the succession of two linear transformations, and this again is well known to be equivalent to the multiplication of the corresponding matrices. In other words, to multiply two dyadics A_1 and A_2 according to (c) is the same thing as multiplying their respective matrices; the algebra of dyadics is the same as the algebra of matrices.

The familiar fact that the matrix of transformation of the element of area is the matrix of cofactors from the matrix of transformation of the lineal elements may be expressed by the formula

$$(6) \qquad (A \cdot V_1) \times (A \cdot V_2) = B \cdot (V_1 \times V_2),$$

where B is the matrix of cofactors of the elements of A. If further, K is the matrix whose cofactors form the elements of A, and if D is its determinant, a fundamental theorem of algebra enables us to rewrite the above equation in the form

$$(6') \qquad (A \cdot V_1) \times (A \cdot V_2) = DK \cdot (V_1 \times V_2).$$

The matrices (or dyadics) A, B, K are in fact connected by the following simple algebraic relations:

$$(6'') \qquad B = DK, \qquad AK_c = DI, \qquad A = DK_c^{-1}$$
$$B_c = D^2 A^{-1},$$

where I is the idemfactor (the dyadic corresponding to the identical transformation), and A^{-1} is the dyadic reciprocal to A (the inverse transformation).

Given any three non-coplanar vectors α, β, γ we define a *reciprocal system* α', β', γ' in order to simplify the expression of certain vector formulæ. The vector α' is taken as normal to the two vectors β, γ in direction, and in value such that $\alpha \cdot \alpha' = 1$. Similarly, β' and γ' are defined so that $\beta' \cdot \alpha = 0$, $\beta' \cdot \beta = 1$, $\beta' \cdot \gamma = 0$, and $\gamma' \cdot \alpha = 0$, $\gamma' \cdot \beta = 0$, $\gamma' \cdot \gamma = 1$. A system of mutually normal unit vectors is self reciprocal.

Consider the resolution of a vector ρ on the three vectors α, β, γ. Such vector components themselves are linear vector functions of ρ, and therefore the dyadic of transformation in each case will be determined if its action on three non-coplanar vectors is known. Let E_1, E_2, E_3 be the three dyadics of transformation. We must have for E_1 the equations

$$E_1 \cdot \alpha = \alpha, \qquad E_1 \cdot \beta = 0, \qquad E_1 \cdot \gamma = 0,$$

which we obtain by considering its action on α, β, γ themselves. These equations are however satisfied by the dyadic $E_1 = \alpha\alpha'$. Hence the formulæ:

(7)
$$E_1 = \alpha\alpha', \qquad E_2 = \beta\beta', \qquad E_3 = \gamma\gamma'.$$

Moreover, since any vector will be the sum of the three components obtained by resolving it in three non-coplanar directions, we have the identity

(8)
$$\rho = (E_1 + E_2 + E_3) \cdot \rho = (\alpha\alpha' + \beta\beta' + \gamma\gamma') \cdot \rho,$$

which is merely another way of saying that the dyadic in parenthesis is the idemfactor I.

23. The Condition of Isogeneity. Let τ be the unit vector in the direction of the curve C at P, and let α, β, τ be the reciprocal system to V_1, V_2, τ. From (7) and (8) we have

(7')
$$E_1 = V_1\alpha, \qquad E_2 = V_2\beta,$$

(8')
$$W_i = (V_1\alpha + V_2\beta) \cdot W_i, \qquad i = 1, 2.$$

From (2) we have

$$\frac{W_2''}{|V_2|} = \frac{W_1'}{|V_1|}, \qquad \frac{W_1''}{|V_2|} = -\frac{W_2'}{|V_1|},$$

whence

$$W_2'' = W_1' \frac{|V_2|}{|V_1|}, \qquad W_2' = -W_1'' \frac{|V_1|}{|V_2|}.$$

Making use of the fact that $E_1 \cdot W_1$ is a vector in the direction of V_1, and that therefore its algebraic magnitude is given by the formula

$$W_1' = \frac{V_1 \cdot E_1 \cdot W_1}{|V_1|},$$

we may rewrite the first of the above equations in the form:

$$W_2'' = \frac{V_1 \cdot E_1 \cdot W_1}{V_1 \cdot V_1} |V_2|,$$

whence, since $E_2 \cdot W_2$ is a vector in the direction V_2, and with reference to the direction of V_2 of algebraic magnitude W_2'', we get:

$$E_2 \cdot W_2 = \frac{V_1 \cdot E_1 \cdot W_1}{V_1 \cdot V_1} V_2.$$

By (7') this reduces at once to the value $E_2 \cdot W_2 = (\alpha \cdot W_1)V_2$.

Similarly $E_1 \cdot W_2 = -(\beta \cdot W_1)V_1$ and therefore by (8') we have the equation

$$W_2 = -(\beta \cdot W_1)V_1 + (\alpha \cdot W_1)V_2,$$

which, in dyadic notation, may be rewritten in the form:

$$(9) \qquad W_2 = -(V_1\beta - V_2\alpha) \cdot W_1.$$

In the same way, or by multiplying both sides of (9) left-handedly by the dyadic $V_1\beta - V_2\alpha$, we get the inverse relation

$$(9') \qquad W_1 = (V_1\beta - V_2\alpha) \cdot W_2.$$

These are the vector forms of the relation (2). *That either* (9) *or* (9') *hold at a given point P and for a given curve C is a necessary and sufficient condition that* $\Phi[C]$ *and* $F[C]$ *be isogenous at P for C.*

We have just shown the necessity of the condition. Let us now show the sufficiency, by calculating directly the quantity $d\Phi/dF$. If we replace $\Delta F_1 + i\Delta F_2$ by $(V_1 + iV_2) \cdot \sigma$ and $\Delta\Phi_1 + i\Delta\Phi_2$ by $(W_1 + iW_2) \cdot \sigma$, we have, from (9) and (8'), the equation

$$(W_1 + iW_2) \cdot \sigma = \sigma \cdot (V_1\alpha + V_2\beta - iV_1\beta + iV_2\alpha) \cdot W_1,$$

of which however the dyadic term factors into two, so that we have the expression

$$\sigma \cdot (V_1 + iV_2)(\alpha - i\beta) \cdot W_1,$$

which is nothing but the product of the two scalar quantities $(V_1 + iV_2) \cdot \sigma$ and $(\alpha - i\beta) \cdot W_1$. We have then the result

$$(10) \qquad \frac{d\Phi}{dF} = (\alpha - i\beta) \cdot W_1,$$

which does not involve the manner in which σ has been allowed to approach zero.

In terms of W_2, instead of W_1, we have the result:

$$(10') \qquad \frac{d\Phi}{dF} = i(\alpha - i\beta) \cdot W_2.$$

In fact, W_1 and W_2 are connected by the relations:

$$(10'') \qquad \begin{aligned} \alpha \cdot W_1 - \beta \cdot W_2 &= 0, \\ \alpha \cdot W_2 + \beta \cdot W_1 &= 0. \end{aligned}$$

§ 2. The Theory of Isogeneity for Additive Functionals

24. The Condition of Isogeneity. We saw in Art. 9 that in the case of additive functionals the vector flux could be chosen as a vector point function, independent of the curve C. Let us assume that V_1, V_2, W_1, W_2 are so chosen, and find the conditions on them in order that Φ and F shall be isogenous complex functionals.

If we take for C a curve which at P is tangent to the plane of V_1 and V_2, the components of these two vectors perpendicular to the curve will lie on the same line. Hence the components of W_1 and W_2 perpendicular to the curve will, as we saw in Art. 21, lie on this same line, and the vectors W_1 and W_2 themselves will lie in the plane of V_1 and V_2. If we indicate with the subscript x the component of a vector in the direction x, and denote the components of the vector product of V_1 and V_2 by D_x, D_y, D_z, i. e.,

$$D_x = V_{1y}V_{2z} - V_{2y}V_{1z}, \text{ etc.},$$

this condition may be written in the form

(11)
$$D_xW_{1x} + D_yW_{1y} + D_zW_{1z} = 0,$$
$$D_xW_{2x} + D_yW_{2y} + D_zW_{2z} = 0,$$

or in the equivalent vector form

(11′)
$$[V_1V_2W_1] = [V_1V_2W_2] = 0.$$

If now we take a new curve, normal at P to the plane of V_1 and V_2, we may apply the analysis of Art. 23, and we find therefore that W_1 and W_2 must satisfy the relation (9). The vectors α, β are now vectors in this common plane of all the vector fluxes, and such that $\alpha \cdot V_1 = 1$, $\alpha \cdot V_2 = 0$, etc. With this understanding, the conditions (9) or (9′) with (11) or (11′) are sufficient, and the formulæ (10) and (10′) give the value of $d\Phi/dF$.

25. The Analog of Laplace's Equation. The question arises as to how much of the functional $\Phi[C]$, isogenous to $F[C]$, is arbitrary, when $F[C]$ is given in advance. It is necessary that the condition of integrability (Lecture I, equation (21′)) be satisfied for both W_1 and W_2. *If R is a vector point function, a necessary and sufficient condition that it be the vector flux of the real or pure imaginary part of a functional $\Phi[C]$, isogenous to $F[C]$, is that it satisfy the equations*

$$[V_1 V_2 R] = 0,$$
$$(12) \qquad \text{Div } R = 0,$$
$$\text{Div } (V_1 \beta - V_2 \alpha) \cdot R = 0.*$$

In fact if we take R as a W_1, the W_2 defined by (9) will satisfy the condition of integrability and lie in the plane of V_1 and V_2. Likewise, if we take R as a W_2, the W_1 defined by (9′) will satisfy the condition of integrability and lie in the plane of V_1 and V_2.

26. A Special Case Connected with the Theory of Laplace's Equation. Consider the case when V_1 and V_2 are unit vectors parallel to the X and Y axes, and therefore independent of x, y, z. For the sake of conciseness in the resulting formulæ, we shall take V_1 in the negative direction of the Y-axis, and V_2 in the positive direction of the X-axis:

$$(13) \qquad V_1 = (0, -1, 0), \qquad V_2 = (1, 0, 0).$$

We have therefore, for the reciprocal system,

$$(13') \qquad \alpha = (0, -1, 0), \qquad \beta = (1, 0, 0),$$

and so the equations (12), which W_1 must satisfy, become:

$$(14) \qquad W_{1z} = 0,$$

$$(14') \qquad \frac{\partial W_{1x}}{\partial x} + \frac{\partial W_{1y}}{\partial y} = 0,$$

$$(14'') \qquad \frac{\partial W_{1y}}{\partial x} - \frac{\partial W_{1x}}{\partial y} = 0.$$

In fact $\alpha \cdot W_1$ is $-W_{1y}$ and $\beta \cdot W_1$ is W_{1x}.

---

* The notation Div R denotes the quantity $(\partial R_x/\partial x) + (\partial R_y/\partial y) + (\partial R_z/\partial z)$, the divergence of R.

The last equation tells us that there is a function $G_1(xyz)$ such that $\partial G_1/\partial x = W_{1x}$ and $\partial G_1/\partial y = W_{1y}$. From (14′) we have

$$(15) \qquad \frac{\partial^2 G_1}{\partial x^2} + \frac{\partial^2 G_1}{\partial y^2} = 0.$$

In the same way, corresponding to W_2, there is a function $G_2(xyz)$ which also satisfies Laplace's equation, with respect to the variables x, y.

The relation between G_1 and G_2 is given to us by means of the relation of isogeneity; in fact, from (9) we have:

$$W_{2x} = - W_{1y}, \qquad W_{2y} = W_{1x},$$

whence

$$(15') \qquad \frac{\partial G_2}{\partial x} = - \frac{\partial G_1}{\partial y}, \qquad \frac{\partial G_2}{\partial y} = \frac{\partial G_1}{\partial x},$$

which are the Cauchy-Riemann equations in the variables x, y.

We may now calculate explicitly the functionals $F[C]$ and $\Phi[C]$. We have:

$$F = \int\int (V_1 + iV_2) \cdot d\sigma$$

where σ is an arbitrary cap of the closed curve C. Hence,

$$F = \int\int - \cos y, n \, d\sigma + i \int\int \cos x, n \, d\sigma.$$

In this expression the positive direction of the normal is taken as the one which stands to positive motion along the curve C in the same relation as that in which the z-axis stands to rotation from the x-axis to the y-axis. Since the direction of positive rotation in the xz-plane is from the z-axis to the x-axis, we have:

$$F = - \int\int_{(\sigma)} dzdx + i \int\int_{(\sigma)} dydz = \int_C dz \int_{(z=\text{const.})} [dx + idy]$$

and finally:

$$(16) \qquad F[C] = \int_C (x + iy)dz.$$

In order to calculate $\Phi[C]$, we have

$$\Phi = \int \int \left\{ \frac{\partial G_1}{\partial x} \cos x, n + \frac{\partial G_1}{\partial y} \cos y, n \right\} d\sigma$$
$$+ i \int \int \left\{ \frac{\partial G_2}{\partial x} \cos x, n + \frac{\partial G_2}{\partial y} \cos y, n \right\} d\sigma,$$

which by (15′) is the same as the equation

$$\Phi = \int \int \left\{ \frac{\partial G_2}{\partial y} \cos x, n - \frac{\partial G_2}{\partial x} \cos y, n - i \frac{\partial G_1}{\partial y} \cos x, n \right.$$
$$\left. + i \frac{\partial G_1}{\partial x} \cos y, n \right\} d\sigma,$$

which again reduces to the following equation:

$$\Phi = \int dz \int \left\{ \frac{\partial G_2}{\partial x} dx + \frac{\partial G_2}{\partial y} dy - i \left(\frac{\partial G_1}{\partial x} dx + \frac{\partial G_1}{\partial y} dy \right) \right\}.$$

But since each of the interior integrals, z being constant, is a curvilinear integral independent of the path, we have

$$\Phi = \int_C \left\{ G_2(xyz) - iG_1(xyz) \right\} dz.$$

On account of the relations (15′), however, the function $G_1 + iG_2$ for a constant value of z is an analytic function of the complex variable $x + iy$. Hence if we write

$$G(x + iy, z) = - i\{G_1(xyz) + iG_2(xyz)\}$$
$$= G_2(xyz) - iG_1(xyz),$$

$G(x + iy, z)$ will be an analytic function of $x + iy$, and *the most general functional isogenous to*

$$F[C] = \int_C (x + iy) dz$$

will be

(16′) $$\Phi[C] = \int_C G(x + iy, z) dz.$$

27. The Analog of Green's Theorem, and Theorems of Determinateness. Consider two complex functionals $\Phi[C]$ and $\Phi'[C]$, both isogenous to the complex functional $F[C]$, and the differential equations

(17) $kW_1 = (V_1V_1 + V_2V_2) \cdot \nabla\varphi_1 + (V_1V_2 - V_2V_1) \cdot \nabla\varphi_2,$

(18) $kW_2 = -(V_1V_2 - V_2V_1) \cdot \nabla\varphi_1 + (V_1V_1 + V_2V_2) \cdot \nabla\varphi_2,$

(19) $kW_1' = (V_1V_1 + V_2V_2) \cdot \nabla\varphi_1' + (V_1V_2 - V_2V_1) \cdot \nabla\varphi_2',$

(20) $kW_2' = -(V_1V_2 - V_2V_1) \cdot \nabla\varphi_1' + (V_1V_1 + V_2V_2) \cdot \nabla\varphi_2',$

which are to be satisfied by certain point functions φ_1, φ_1', φ_2, φ_2', as yet undetermined. In these equations W_1, W_2 and W_1', W_2' are the vector fluxes of Φ and Φ' respectively, $\nabla\varphi_1$ denotes the vector $(\partial\varphi_1/\partial x, \partial\varphi_1/\partial y, \partial\varphi_1/\partial z)$, etc., and k is a point function $k(xyz)$, at present not further specified.

If we multiply both sides of (17) left-handedly by the dyadic $-(V_1\beta - V_2\alpha)$, the resulting equation reduces to (18). Similarly (20) is a consequence of (19).

If α, β, γ are any three vectors, a much used formula in vector analysis gives us the equations*

$$\alpha \times (\beta \times \gamma) = -(\beta \times \gamma) \times \alpha$$
$$= \alpha \cdot \gamma\beta - \alpha \cdot \beta\gamma = (\beta\gamma - \gamma\beta) \cdot \alpha.$$

Hence we can rewrite equations (17) to (20) in the form:

(17') $kW_1 = (V_1V_1 + V_2V_2) \cdot \nabla\varphi_1 + \nabla\varphi_2 \times (V_1 \times V_2),$

(18') $kW_2 = -\nabla\varphi_1' \times (V_1 \times V_2) + (V_1V_1 + V_2V_2) \cdot \nabla\varphi_2',$

etc.

In connection with the equations (17) to (20) or (17') to (20'), we consider a certain scalar invariant $H_{\Phi_1\Phi_1'}$ defined by the equation

(21) $(V_1 \times V_2)H_{\Phi_1\Phi_1'} = W_1 \times W_2',$

where the left- and right-hand members represent, of course, in virtue of (11) or (11'), collinear vectors. If in this equation we substitute for W_1 its value as given by (17'), we obtain the relation

$$k(V_1 \times V_2)H_{\Phi_1\Phi_1'} = (V_1 \times W_2')(V_1 \cdot \nabla\varphi_1)$$
$$+ (V_2 \times W_2')(V_2 \cdot \nabla\varphi_1) + \{\nabla\varphi_2 \times (V_1 \times V_2)\} \times W_2'.$$

---

* Gibbs-Wilson, Vector analysis, New York (1901), p. 74.

The above quoted vector formula gives us for the last term of this equation the equivalent form

$$- W_2' \times \{\nabla\varphi_2 \times (V_1 \times V_2)\} = - \{W_2' \cdot (V_1 \times V_2)\}\nabla\varphi_2$$
$$+ (W_2' \cdot \nabla\varphi_2)(V_1 \times V_2).$$

and in this expression the first term vanishes, since W_2' lies in the plane of V_1 and V_2. Moreover from (9) we have

$$V_1 \times W_2' = (V_1 \times V_2)\alpha \cdot W_1',$$
$$V_2 \times W_2' = - (V_2 \times V_1)\beta \cdot W_1' - (V_1 \times V_2)\beta \cdot W_1',$$

since $V_1 \times V_1 = 0$ and $V_2 \times V_2 = 0$. Hence our equation becomes

$$k(V_1 \times V_2)H_{\Phi_1\Phi_1'} = (V_1 \times V_2)\{(\alpha \cdot W_1')(V_1 \cdot \nabla\varphi_1)$$
$$+ (\beta \cdot W_1')(V_2 \cdot \nabla\varphi_1) + W_2' \cdot \nabla\varphi_2\},$$

or

$$kH_{\Phi_1\Phi_1'} = \nabla\varphi_1 \cdot (V_1\alpha + V_2\beta) \cdot W_1' + W_2' \cdot \nabla\varphi_2.$$

By means of the identity (8′), however, this reduces to the formula

$$(22) \qquad kH_{\Phi_1\Phi_1'} = W_1' \cdot \nabla\varphi_1 + W_2' \cdot \nabla\varphi_2.$$

Also, in the same way, eliminating W_2' instead of W_1, from 21, we have

$$(22') \qquad kH_{\phi_1\Phi_1'} = W_1 \cdot \nabla\varphi_1' + W_2 \cdot \nabla\varphi_2'.$$

The function $H_{\Phi_1\Phi_1'}$, from its definition in (21), is seen to be the ratio of the areas of the two parallelograms, one with sides W_1 and W_2', the other with sides V_1 and V_2.

If we take $\Phi_1' = \Phi_1$, denoting $H_{\Phi_1\Phi_1'}$ by Θ_{Φ_1}, we have the equation

$$(23) \qquad (V_1 \times V_2)\Theta_{\Phi_1} = W_1 \times W_2.$$

It is not hard to see that the quantity Θ_{Φ_1} is essentially positive. In fact, from (9) we have

$$W_1 \times W_2 = - (W_1 \times V_1)(\beta \cdot W_1) + (W_1 \times V_2)(\alpha \cdot W_1)$$

and this, by means of the identity (8′), becomes

$$(V_1 \times V_2)(\beta \cdot W_1)^2 + (V_1 \times V_2)(\alpha \cdot W_1)^2$$

so that we have

$$\Theta_{\Phi_1} = (\alpha \cdot W_1)^2 + (\beta \cdot W_1)^2$$

a quantity that is essentially not negative.

It is worth while perhaps to rewrite the formulæ (22), (22') without the use of vectors. They may in fact be written as follows:

$$kH_{\Phi_1\Phi_1'} = W_{1x}'\frac{\partial \varphi_1}{\partial x} + W_{1y}'\frac{\partial \varphi_1}{\partial y} + W_{1z}'\frac{\partial \varphi_1}{\partial z}$$

$$+ W_{2x}'\frac{\partial \varphi_2}{\partial x} + W_{2y}'\frac{\partial \varphi_2}{\partial y} + W_{2z}'\frac{\partial \varphi_2}{\partial z}$$

$$= W_{1x}\frac{\partial \varphi_1'}{\partial x} + W_{1y}\frac{\partial \varphi_1'}{\partial y} + W_{1z}\frac{\partial \varphi_1'}{\partial z}$$

$$+ W_{2x}\frac{\partial \varphi_2'}{\partial x} + W_{2y}\frac{\partial \varphi_2'}{\partial y} + W_{2z}\frac{\partial \varphi_2'}{\partial z}.$$

If we integrate both sides of these equations over a region S enclosed in a surface σ, and perform the suggested integration by parts we obtain the formulæ ($d\sigma$ as a vector having the direction of the interior normal):

$$(24) \qquad \iiint kH dS = - \iint [\varphi_1 W_1' \cdot d\sigma + \varphi_2 W_2' \cdot d\sigma]$$

$$= - \iint [\varphi_1' W_1 \cdot d\sigma + \varphi_2' W_2 \cdot d\sigma],$$

$$(25) \qquad \iiint k\Theta dS = - \iint [\varphi_1 W_1 \cdot d\sigma + \varphi_2 W_2 \cdot d\sigma].$$

These are the analogs of Green's theorem for the operator of Laplace.

From these equations, Volterra is able to obtain certain theorems of determinateness analogous to the well-known facts about the uniqueness of harmonic functions which take on given values along closed curves. He assumes that (17), equivalent to two linear partial differential equations of the first order in φ_1 and φ_2, admits solutions, continuous with their first partial derivatives, within a given region, when the function $k(xyz)$ has been chosen continuously of one sign; this sign without loss of generality, being taken as positive. By writing then

$\Phi_1' = \Phi_1$, in equations (17) to (20), he is able to deduce the following theorem.

Let $\Phi[C] = \Phi_1[C] + i\Phi_2[C]$ *be isogenous to* $F[C] = F_1[C] + iF_2[C]$, *and without singularities within a closed surface* σ.* *Then, if the values of* $\Phi[C]$ *are known for all the closed curves which lie on* σ, *the functional* $\Phi[C]$ *will be determined for all the closed curves of the region* S, *enclosed by* σ.

In fact, suppose there were two such functionals, and let $\Phi''[C]$ be their difference. The quantities $W_1'' \cdot d\sigma$ and $W_2'' \cdot d\sigma$ will vanish at every point of σ. Hence if we apply the equation (25) to $\Phi''[C]$, the right-hand member will vanish, and we shall have

$$\iiint k\Theta dS = 0,$$

where the integration is carried out over the region S. But since k is positive and Θ is nowhere negative, Θ must be identically zero. This implies however (provided that V_1 and V_2 are not collinear) that W_1'' and W_2'' vanish identically, and hence $\Phi''[C]$ must vanish identically.

28. Transformation of the Variables x, y, z. Make a transformation of coordinates $x = x(\bar{x}\bar{y}\bar{z})$, $y = y(\bar{x}\bar{y}\bar{z})$, $z = z(\bar{x}\bar{y}\bar{z})$, whose Jacobian $D = \partial(xyz)/\partial(\bar{x}\bar{y}\bar{z})$ does not vanish; denote by K the matrix and dyadic corresponding to D:

$$(26) \qquad K = \begin{bmatrix} \dfrac{\partial x}{\partial \bar{x}} & \dfrac{\partial y}{\partial \bar{x}} & \dfrac{\partial z}{\partial \bar{x}} \\[2mm] \dfrac{\partial x}{\partial \bar{y}} & \dfrac{\partial y}{\partial \bar{y}} & \dfrac{\partial z}{\partial \bar{y}} \\[2mm] \dfrac{\partial x}{\partial \bar{z}} & \dfrac{\partial y}{\partial \bar{z}} & \dfrac{\partial z}{\partial \bar{z}} \end{bmatrix},$$

and by A the matrix of the cofactors of the elements of K, that is, the matrix of the quantities $\partial(yz)/\partial(\bar{y}\bar{z})$, etc.

According to (6'') we have $A = DK_c^{-1}$, and according to (22), Lecture I, any vector flux V is transformed by the formula

$$(27) \qquad \bar{V} = A \cdot V.$$

* The vector W_1 is assumed to be continuous within and on the surface σ and its components to have continuous partial derivatives of the first order at all points inside σ.

The relation of isogeneity is preserved by the transformation. In fact, coplanar vectors, transformed by any linear vector function, remain coplanar; and therefore $\overline{W}_1$ and $\overline{W}_2$ are coplanar with $\overline{V}_1$ and $\overline{V}_2$. Moreover the condition (9) is satisfied. To see this let $\overline{\alpha}$ and $\overline{\beta}$ be the plane system reciprocal to $\overline{V}_1$ and $\overline{V}_2$. We have then

$$(28) \qquad \overline{\alpha} = \alpha \cdot A^{-1}, \qquad \overline{\beta} = \beta \cdot A^{-1},$$

whence $\overline{\beta} \cdot \overline{W}_1 = \beta \cdot W_1$ and $\overline{\alpha} \cdot \overline{W}_1 = \alpha \cdot W_1$, and therefore, with the aid of (27),

$$- (\overline{V}_1 \overline{\beta} - \overline{V}_2 \alpha) \cdot \overline{W}_1 = A \cdot \{ - (V_1 \beta - V_2 \alpha) \cdot W_1 = A \cdot W_2 = \overline{W}_2,$$

and the condition of isogeneity is satisfied. This fact may also be established by means of P. Lévy's geometrical interpretation.

The quantity $H_{\Phi_1 \Phi_1'}$ is absolutely invariant of the transformation. If we multiply left-handedly both members of (21), which defines $H_{\Phi_1 \Phi_1'}$, by the dyadic $B = DK$, the equation reduces by (6′) to the result:

$$(\overline{V}_1 \times \overline{V}_2) H_{\Phi_1 \Phi_1'} = \overline{W}_1 \times \overline{W}_2'.$$

But this is the equation which defines $\overline{H}_{\Phi_1 \Phi_1'}$; and therefore

$$\overline{H}_{\Phi_1 \Phi_1'} = H_{\Phi_1 \Phi_1'}.$$

We may also investigate the covariance of the equations (17) to (20). The vector elements of arc in the two spaces, $d\rho$ and $d\rho'$, are connected by the relation

$$(29) \qquad d\rho = \overline{d\rho} \cdot K = K_c \cdot \overline{d\rho}.$$

Let $\varphi(xyz)$ be any scalar point function; since

$$d\varphi = \nabla\varphi \cdot d\rho = \overline{\nabla}\varphi \cdot \overline{d\rho},$$

it follows from (29) that:

$$(29') \qquad \overline{\nabla}\varphi = \nabla\varphi \cdot K_c = K \cdot \nabla\varphi.$$

If we apply these results to the equations (17) to (20), we see that these equations will remain satisfied in the transformed space by the functions φ_1, φ_1', φ_2, φ_2', provided that we take

$$(30) \qquad \overline{k} = \frac{\partial(xyz)}{\partial(\overline{x}\overline{y}\overline{z})} \, k.$$

An interesting result is connected with the total differential equation

$$(31) \qquad D_x dx + D_y dy + D_z dz = 0,$$

or

$$[d\rho V_1 V_2] = 0.$$

We have,

$$[\overline{d\rho}\,\overline{V}_1\overline{V}_2] = \overline{d\rho} \cdot (\overline{V}_1 \times \overline{V}_2) = D\overline{d\rho} \cdot K \cdot (V_1 \times V_2) = Dd\rho \cdot (V_1 \times V_2),$$

and therefore, from (29), we have the equation

$$(32) \qquad [\overline{d\rho}\,\overline{V}_1\overline{V}_2] = \frac{\partial(xyz)}{\partial(\overline{xyz})} [d\rho V_1 V_2].$$

If then the equation (31) is satisfied, it remains satisfied after the transormation. Hence if (31) is integrable, it is transformed into an integrable equation.

In this case, that is, if $F[C]$ is such a complex functional that (31) is integrable, Volterra shows that the equations (17) to (20) can be satisfied in a specially simple manner; namely, by taking $\varphi_1 \equiv \varphi_1' \equiv 0$, and choosing φ_2 and φ_2' to satisfy the thus simplified equations, or vice versa, by putting $\varphi_2 \equiv \varphi_2' \equiv 0$. *A transformation may then be found which changes $F[C]$ into the form discussed in Art. 26.*

29. Functional Integration and Cauchy's Theorem.

Let $\Phi[C]$ be isogenous to $F[C]$. This relation may be stated in the form

$$(32) \qquad W = fV,$$

where $f = f_1(xyz) + if_2(xyz)$ is some scalar point function. Since the divergence of W must vanish, it follows that we must have

$$(33) \qquad \nabla f \cdot V = 0.$$

If the relation (33) is satisfied, the functional $F[C]$ and the function f are said to be isogenous.

If any functional Φ' is isogenous to F, it is also isogenous to f, for in this case there will be an f' such that $W' = f'V$, whence

$$\nabla f \cdot W' = f' \nabla f \cdot V = 0.$$

Let us denote by $dF/d\sigma$ the vector $V = V_1 + iV_2$, and consider the quantity

$$(34) \qquad \Phi[C] = \iint\limits_{(C)} f \frac{dF}{d\sigma} \cdot d\sigma,$$

where σ is a cap of the closed curve C, and $F[C]$ and $f(xyz)$ are isogenous. Equation (34) really defines a functional of C, as is implied by the notation. For this, it is sufficient that

$$\text{Div } [fdF/d\sigma] \equiv 0.$$

This condition is satisfied since we have

$$\text{Div } \left(f\frac{dF}{d\sigma} \right) = f \text{ Div } V + \nabla f \cdot V.$$

The notation

(35) $$\Phi[C] = \int fdF$$

is used by Volterra to denote the integral (34). If the field of integration is a closed surface, or a complete surface boundary to a region, we have the result:

(36) $$\int fdF = 0,$$

which is a generalization of Cauchy's theorem for functions of a single complex variable.

§ 3. Isogenous Non-Additive Functionals

30. The Condition of Isogeneity. The condition of isogeneity for non-additive functionals has already been obtained in terms of the vector flux V, or rather, in terms of its component normal to the curve. It is desirable to express the same condition in terms of the functional derivative vectors, which are uniquely determined in terms of the curve and the point where the differentiation takes place.

Denote by $R_1[C \mid M]$, $R_2[C \mid M]$ the vector derivatives of $F_1[C]$ and $F_2[C]$ respectively, and by $U_1[C \mid M]$ and $U_2[C \mid M]$ the vector derivatives of $\Phi_1[C]$ and $\Phi_2[C]$; so that we have

(37) $$R = R_1 + iR_2, \qquad U = U_1 + iU_2.$$

If we denote by τ the unit vector in the direction of the curve, and let V and W be the normal components of the vector fluxes, we shall, as we saw in Lecture I, have the relations

(38) $$R = \tau \times V, \qquad U = \tau \times W.$$

Form now the vector product, multiplying τ left-handedly on to the equation (9); we have

$$U_2 = - (R_1\beta - R_2\alpha) \cdot W_1.$$

Let us denote by β' a vector perpendicular to τ, such that $\beta = \beta' \times \tau$ and by α' a similar vector such that $\alpha = \alpha' \times \tau$. We have

$$\beta \cdot W_1 = \beta' \times \tau \cdot W_1 = [\beta'\tau W_1] = \beta' \cdot \tau \times W_1 = \beta' \cdot U_1,$$

and therefore, treating $\alpha \cdot W_1$ in the same way,

(39) $$U_2 = - (R_1\beta' - R_2\alpha') \cdot U_1.$$

The equation (39) *is the condition of isogeneity. The vectors* α', β', τ *form the reciprocal system to the vectors* R_1, R_2, τ, *and* α', β' *are given by the formulæ*

(40)
$$\alpha' = \tau \times \alpha, \qquad \beta' = \tau \times \beta,$$
$$\alpha = \alpha' \times \tau, \qquad \beta = \beta' \times \tau.$$

In fact, if $\beta = \beta' \times \tau$, we have $\tau \times \beta = \tau \times (\beta' \times \tau)$ which may be expressed in the form $\tau \cdot \tau \beta' - \tau \cdot \beta' \tau$ (see Art. 27, footnote). This last expression reduces however to β', since τ is normal to β', and therefore $\tau \cdot \beta' = 0$. Hence $\tau \times \beta = \beta'$. Conversely, if $\tau \times \beta = \beta'$ it follows that $\beta = \beta' \times \tau$; and similar relations may be shown in the same way to hold between α and α'.

In order to show that $\alpha' \ \beta' \ \tau$ is the reciprocal system to $R_1 \ R_2 \ \tau$, we must show that $R_1 \cdot \alpha' = 1$, $R_1 \cdot \beta' = 0$, $R_2 \cdot \alpha' = 0$, $R_2 \cdot \beta' = 1$, the other necessary relations being obvious. We have $R_1 \cdot \alpha' = (\tau \times V_1) \cdot (\tau \times \beta)$ and this, by a formula in vector analysis,* is $(\tau \cdot \tau)(V_1 \cdot \beta) - (\tau \cdot \beta)(V_1 \cdot \tau)$, which is $V_1 \cdot \beta$, which is 1. Similarly, the other relations are established. Thus the theorem is proved.

The equation (39) may be established geometrically, in the same way as (2) was established.

31. Transformation of the Variables x, y, z. According to equation (23) of Lecture I, we have

(41)
$$\overline{R} = K \cdot R \frac{ds}{d\overline{s}},$$

where K is the matrix or dyadic K already defined, and ds and $d\overline{s}$ are corresponding elements of arc. It follows that the relation of isogeneity is invariant of the transformation. In fact, multiplying (39) left-handedly by the dyadic K, we have

$$\overline{U}_2 = - (\overline{R}_1 \beta' - \overline{R}_2 \alpha') \cdot U_1.$$

If we define the quantities

$$\overline{\alpha}' = \alpha' \cdot K \frac{ds}{d\overline{s}}, \qquad \overline{\beta}' = \beta' \cdot K \frac{ds}{d\overline{s}},$$

they will be reciprocal to $\overline{R}_1$ and $\overline{R}_2$, in the new reciprocal system. Moreover

$$\alpha' = \overline{\alpha}' \cdot K^{-1} \frac{d\overline{s}}{ds}, \qquad \beta' = \overline{\beta}' \cdot K^{-1} \frac{d\overline{s}}{ds},$$

so that $\overline{\alpha}' \cdot \overline{U}_1 = \alpha' \cdot U_1$ and $\overline{\beta}' \cdot \overline{U}_1 = \beta' \cdot U_1$, and finally:

$$\overline{U}_2 = - (\overline{R}_1 \overline{\beta}' - \overline{R}_2 \overline{\beta}') \cdot U_1,$$

which is the relation of isogeneity in the transformed space.

32. Functional Integration and Cauchy's Theorem. A real vector functional $R[C \mid M]$ can represent the vector derivative of a functional $F[C]$ only if certain *conditions of integrability* are satisfied. In case each of the three components of $R[C \mid M]$ has itself at every point M_1 of C a true derivative (e. g., $S_x[C \mid MM_1]$ is the vector derivative of the x-component of $R[C \mid M]$, taken at the point M_1), the conditions of integrability are given by Volterra as follows:

* Gibbs-Wilson, Vector analysis, New York (1901), p. 76.

$$(42) \quad \begin{cases} R[C \mid M] \cdot \tau = 0, \\ S_x[C \mid MM_1] \cdot \tau_1 = 0, \qquad S_y[C \mid MM_1] \cdot \tau_1 = 0, \qquad S_z[C \mid MM_1] \cdot \tau_1 = 0, \end{cases}$$

where τ represents the unit vector in the direction of the curve at M, and τ_1 the same quantity at M_1;

$$(43) \qquad S_{xx}[C \mid MM_1] = S_{xx}[C \mid M_1 M],$$

$$(44) \qquad S_{yz}[C \mid MM_1] = S_{zy}[C \mid M_1 M], \qquad \text{etc.},$$

where S_{yz} represents the z-component of S_y, etc.*

A complex vector functional $R = R_1 + iR_2$ can represent the vector derivative of a complex functional $F = F_1 + iF_2$, only if R_1 is the derivative of F_1 and R_2 is the derivative of F_2. In the special case just considered, the relations (42), (43), (44) will be satisfied for both real vectors R_1 and R_2, if they are satisfied for the complex vector R, and vice versa.

Let us speak of a scalar functional $\Theta[C \mid M]$ as an *integrand* for a scalar functional $F[C]$, if the vector $\Theta[C \mid M]R[C \mid M]$ satisfies the conditions of integrability. In the special case mentioned in the preceding paragraph, the equations (42) are automatically satisfied, so the conditions of integrability refer merely to (43) and (44).

If $\Theta[C \mid M]$ is an integrand for $F[C]$, there is a functional $\Phi[C]$ whose vector derivative is $\Theta[C \mid M]R[C \mid M]$. In fact:

$$(45) \qquad \Phi[C] = \int \int \Theta[C \mid M]R[C \mid M] \cdot d\sigma + h,$$

where the integration is extended over a cap of C, or over a cap joining a fixed curve C_0 to the variable curve C, and h is an arbitrary constant.

The equation (45) may be written in the form

$$(45') \qquad \Phi[C] - \Phi[C_0] = \int \int \Theta[C \mid M] \frac{dF}{d\sigma} \cdot d\sigma = \int \Theta dF,$$

where $dF/d\sigma$ denotes $R[C \mid M]$. If we define:

$$\frac{d\Psi}{dF} = \frac{\dfrac{d\Psi}{d\sigma}}{\dfrac{dF}{d\sigma}},$$

where $\Psi[C]$ and $F[C]$ are any two isogenous functionals, we shall have $d\Psi/dF$ a scalar functional of C, M. Hence we have the formula

$$(46) \qquad \int \Theta dF = \int \Theta \frac{dF}{d\Psi} d\Psi.$$

If Θ is an integrand for F, and Ψ and F are isogenous, then $\Theta(dF/d\Psi)$ will be an integrand for Ψ.

The relations (45'), (46) are invariant of a transformation of spaces. For a closed surface, which does not contain singularities:

$$(47) \qquad \int \Theta dF = 0.$$

* Volterra, *Rendiconti della R. Accademia dei Lincei*, vol. III (1887), 2e semestre, p. 229.

§ 4. ADDITIVE COMPLEX FUNCTIONALS OF HYPERSPACES

33. Elementary Functionals.   Volterra develops the theory of additive complex functionals of which the arguments are r-dimensional hyperspaces immersed in an n-space.   For $r = n - 2$, the theory is a direct generalization of the theory of complex functionals of curves in 3-space; but for $r < n - 2$ the problem of finding a functional isogenous to a given one involves solving a system of partial differential equations where there are more equations than unknowns.   That problem will then be expressed in this form: what conditions must be satisfied by $F[C]$ in order that

$$d\Phi_1 + id\Phi_2 = f(dF_1 + idF_2)$$

may be the differential of an additive functional of hyperspaces $\Phi[S_r]$, with f a point function?

This condition is expressed by a certain system of linear partial differential equations, of which the coefficients depend on F, in the dependent variable f.   These equations may be incompatible, and admit no solution other than a constant.   If the functional $F[S_r]$ has been chosen however in such a way as to make the system *completely integrable*, the functional $F[S_r]$ is said to be *elementary*.   Elementary functionals are not the only ones which can have functionals related to them isogenously, since every functional is isogenous to a constant times itself.

34. Integrals of Analytic Functions of Two Complex Variables. The case $n = 4$, $r = 1$ is interesting, because it is related to the theory of integrals of functions of two complex variables.*   Consider in fact a surface integral:

$$(48) \qquad \int\int F[\xi, \eta]d\xi d\eta,$$

which is written as

$$(49) \quad \int\int \{(P + iQ)dxdz + (iP - Q)dxdt$$
$$+ (iP - Q)dydz - (P + iQ)dydt\},$$

* For a summary of this subject see Osgood: Madison Colloquium, New York (1914), p. 136. The author discusses the possibilities for the region at ∞.

the result obtained by carrying out in formal fashion the multiplication indicated when we put $\xi = x + iy$, $\eta = z + it$. In order to make our intuition clear, we can imagine the two-dimensional locus as enclosed in a three-dimensional space, and the integration as carried out over a surface in that 3-space.

The integral (49) is defined in terms of curvilinear coordinates u, v on the surface. Thus

$$dxdz = \frac{\partial(xz)}{\partial(uv)} dudv = -dzdx.$$

Poincaré showed that the necessary and sufficient condition that the integral (49) be independent of the surface, i. e., depend merely upon the closed curve of which it is the cap, is that $P + iQ$ be an analytic function of $x + iy$ and $z + it$. In this case, therefore, the quantities defined by (49) represent additive complex functionals of curves in 4-space. Singular surfaces (or singular curves as cut from them by the Poincaré 3-space) may be cut or looped by these curves.[*]

Any two additive complex functionals of the type just defined will be isogenous. In fact, if $F[C]$ is one such functional and $F'[C]$ another, the condition to be satisfied is:

$$\frac{dF'}{dF} = f(xyzt),$$

in which the function f does not depend upon the manner of letting the change σ, given to C, approach zero. But as we see from (49), we have always

$$\frac{dF'}{dF} = \frac{P' + iQ'}{P + iQ}.$$

It may be deduced in an equally simple manner that $F[C]$ is *elementary*. If in (49) we substitute fF for F, where $f = f_1(xyzt) + if_2(xyzt)$, it is merely necessary to write conditions that the new integral be independent of the surface. These are:

---

[*] Volterra remarks that the "point of departure" of his study of complex valued functions of curves was Poincaré's *Acta* memoir (cited p. 30). A more detailed account of the latter is given in the Appendix.

(50)
$$\frac{\partial(fF)}{\partial x} + i\,\frac{\partial(fF)}{\partial y} = 0,$$
$$\frac{\partial(fF)}{\partial z} + i\,\frac{\partial(fF)}{\partial t} = 0,$$

where already

(51)
$$\frac{\partial F}{\partial x} + i\,\frac{\partial F}{\partial y} = 0,$$
$$\frac{\partial F}{\partial z} + i\,\frac{\partial F}{\partial t} = 0.$$

Therefore, for ξ, η such that $F(\xi\,\eta) \neq 0$, the conditions reduce to the following:

$$\frac{\partial f}{\partial x} + i\,\frac{\partial f}{\partial y} = 0,$$

$$\frac{\partial f}{\partial z} + i\,\frac{\partial f}{\partial t} = 0,$$

and yield the result that f must be an analytic function of ξ and η. But since, for their solution, no condition is imposed on $F[C]$, it follows that $F[C]$ is already elementary.

The theory of isogenous additive functionals of curves in 4-space includes more however than the theory of surface integrals of analytic functions of two complex variables; for the integral (49) contains no terms in $dx\,dy$ or $dz\,dt$. The theory thus will provide an extension of many properties to the general class of elementary functionals of curves in 4-space.

In general, for the consideration of r-functionals in n-space, we may enclose them in spaces of dimension $r + 2$; and in the $(r + 2)$-space apply the theory of functionals of curves in 3-space. When the functionals are elementary there will be important properties (like the generalization of Cauchy's theorem) which will be invariant of the $(r + 2)$-space in which the r-spaces may be enclosed.

LECTURE III.

IMPLICIT FUNCTIONAL EQUATIONS*

§ 1. The Method of Successive Approximations

35. An Introductory Theorem. An implicit functional equation which is easily solvable is the following:

$$(1) \qquad\qquad \varphi(x) = F[\varphi(\overset{b}{\underset{a}{s}}) \,|\, x],$$

where, besides depending on the function φ and the variable x, the functional constituting the right-hand member may depend upon other functions f, g, $\cdots$ and other variables y, z, $\cdots$, appearing parametrically. The equation (1) may be solved immediately by the method of successive approximations, and in fact serves, with the conditions imposed upon it, rather as a convenient formulation of that method than as a theorem of explicit value.

Consider a class L of limited functions $\varphi(x)$, which contains the limit function of any uniformly convergent sequence of its functions $\varphi_n(x)$. Such a class is for instance the totality of continuous functions, in numerical value less than or equal to a given constant.

In regard to the functional F we assume:

(*i*) If $\varphi(x)$ is a function of L, then $F[\varphi \,|\, x]$ is a function of L.

(*ii*) The functional F satisfies a Cauchy-Lipschitz condition:

* This lecture is based on the following references:

Volterra, Leçons sur les fonctions de lignes, Paris (1913), chapter 4.

Hadamard, Leçons sur le calcul des variations, Paris (1910), chapter 7, Book II.

Riesz, Les opérations fonctionelles linéaires, *Annales Scientifiques de l'École Normale Supérieure*, vol. 31 (1914), pp. 9–14.

Lebesgue, Sur l'intégrale de Stieltjes et sur les opérations fonctionelles linéaires, *Comptes Rendus*, vol. 150 (1910), pp. 86–88.

Evans, Some general types of functional equations, *Proceedings of the Fifth International Congress of Mathematicians*, Cambridge (1912), vol. 1, pp. 385–396.

namely, if φ_1 and φ_2 are any two functions of L, then a constant M can be found, $M < 1$, such that the following condition holds:

$$(2) \quad \max_a^b \left| F[\varphi_1(s) \,|\, x] - F[\varphi_2(s) \,|\, x] \right| \leq M \max_a^b \left| \varphi_1(x) - \varphi_2(x) \right|,$$

where $\max_a^b |\varphi(x)|$ denotes the upper bound of a function $\varphi(x)$ in the range ab.

Under these conditions, the class L contains one and only one solution of equation (1).

To construct this solution we take φ_0, any particular function in L, and write

$$\varphi_n(x) = F[\varphi_{n-1} \,|\, x], \qquad n = 1, 2, 3, \cdots.$$

Then the function

$$\varphi(x) = \lim_{n=\infty} \varphi_n(x)$$

is in L, as is seen at once from the uniform convergence of the series

$$\varphi_0 + (\varphi_1 - \varphi_0) + (\varphi_2 - \varphi_1) + \cdots,$$

and is a solution of (1), since

$$\max_a^b \left| \varphi - F[\varphi \,|\, x] \right| \leq \max_a^b \left| \varphi - \varphi_{n+1} \right| + \max_a^b \left| F[\varphi_n \,|\, x] - F[\varphi \,|\, x]. \right.$$

If there were two solutions φ and φ' we should have, by equation (2):

$$\max_a^b \left| \varphi - \varphi' \right| \leq M \max_a^b \left| \varphi - \varphi' \right|,$$

which is a contradiction, since $M < 1$.

We have the corollary, that if L contains a continuous function, and if $F[\varphi \,|\, x]$ represents a continuous function of x when its argument $\varphi(x)$ represents a continuous function of x, then the unique solution of (1) is continuous.

36. The Case of a Variable Upper Limit. If the functional $F[\varphi \,|\, x]$ depends upon φ only for values between a and x, we are able to make use of a property of *prolongation*, which, speaking generally, makes less restrictive the convergence condition *(ii)* imposed on M in Art. 35. In particular, if F consists of terms independent of φ plus a term whose variation is of the form

$$\int_a^x F'[\varphi(\overset{x}{\underset{a}{s}}) \mid x'x]\delta\varphi(x')dx'$$

the variation of F due to a change of φ can be made as small as we please by taking x close enough to a.

Consider then the equation

(3) $$\varphi(x) = F[\varphi(\overset{x}{\underset{a}{s}}) \mid x]$$

and in connection with it a class L' of limited functions $\varphi(x)$. We shall assume that if $\varphi_n(x)$ (φ_n being of L') approaches a function $\varphi(x)$ uniformly in an interval x_1x_2, open or closed, then $\varphi(x)$ is of L'. It may not be defined outside of x_1x_2; we shall assume, however, that we can find another function over the rest of ab so that $\varphi(x)$ as extended by this function will be for the whole interval ab a member of L'.

In regard to the functional F we assume that a finite number of points $a = a_0, a_1, a_2 \cdots a_k = b$ can be found so that the following conditions hold:

(i) If $\varphi(x)$ is a function of L' in the interval $a \leqq x < a_{i+1}$, and satisfies equation (3) in the interval $a \leqq x < a_i$, then in the interval $a \leqq x < a_{i+1}$ the quantity $F[\varphi \mid x]$ represents a function in L'.

(ii) If $\varphi_1(x)$ and $\varphi_2(x)$ are functions of L' in the interval $a \leqq x < a_{i+1}$, and satisfy the equation

$$\varphi_1(x) = \varphi_2(x) = F[\varphi_1 \mid x]$$

in the interval $a \leqq x < a_i$, then in the interval $a \leqq x < a_{i+1}$, we have the Cauchy-Lipschitz condition:

(4) $$\overset{x}{\underset{a}{\max}} \mid F[\varphi_1(\overset{x}{\underset{a}{s}}) \mid x] - F[\varphi_2(\overset{x}{\underset{a}{s}}) \mid x] \mid \; \leqq M \overset{x}{\underset{a}{\max}} \mid \varphi_1(x) - \varphi_2(x) \mid ,$$

in which M is some constant, less than unity.

Under these conditions, the class L' contains one and only one solution of (3), *in the interval $a \leqq x < b$.* The proof of this theorem is the same as that of Art. 35.

We have a true theorem if throughout (i), (ii) and the above conclusion we change the sign $<$ wherever it occurs, to the sign $\leqq$. We can deduce directly the corollary of this last theorem, that if L' contains a function which is continuous $a \leqq x \leqq a_1$, and a function which, when φ is given as continuous $a \leqq x \leqq a_i$, extends it continuously through the interval $a \leqq x \leqq a_{i+1}$, and if F represents a continuous function of x when its argument φ is a continuous function of x, then the unique solution of (3) is continuous through the interval $a \leqq x \leqq b$.

The theorems of this article and the preceding one serve to establish the existence of the solutions of differential equations and integral equations of general types, without a restriction of linearity. More general theorems than these may easily be obtained, by replacing the functional *max* by some such thing as $\int \mid \varphi_1 - \varphi_2 \mid dx$, or by some more general functional such as the *norm* of A. A. Bennett,[*] or the *modulus* of E. H. Moore.[†]   Gain of generality

---

[*] A. A. Bennett, *Proceedings of the National Academy of Sciences*, vol. 2 (1916), pp. 592–598.

[†] See Lecture V, General Analysis.

usually implies less immediate applicability to special cases, and the above theorems are sufficient for the cases which we are to consider. They supplant the repetition of the analysis of successive approximations in those cases.

§ 2. The Linear Functional

37. Hadamard's Representation. The resolution of an implicit equation in several variables for the purpose of determining one variable as a function of the others depends in the non-special case upon the linear relation which holds between the differentials of the variables involved. Likewise for the study of implicit equations in *functionals* in general, a study of the linear functional is first necessary. It is the purpose of this section to show that under very general conditions the restriction of linearity implies that the functional can be written explicitly, in terms of the limit of an integral, as found by Hadamard; a Stieltjes integral, as found by F. Riesz; a Lebesgue integral, as rewritten by Lebesgue. Of these forms the first is slightly more general than the others; although here the same hypotheses are used for all three.

We consider a functional

$$(5) \qquad T[\overset{b}{\underset{a}{\varphi(x)}}]$$

operating on any function continuous, $a \leq x \leq b$, and assume that the functional is linear, that is, such that:

$$(6) \qquad T[c_1\varphi_1 + c_2\varphi_2] = c_1 T[\varphi_1] + c_2 T[\varphi_2],$$

and also that it is continuous in regard to its argument φ, or what, on account of the postulate of linearity, evidently amounts to the same thing, satisfies a condition of the form:

$$(7) \qquad |T[\varphi]| \leq M \max_{a}^{b} |\varphi(x)|$$

in which M is some constant.*

There is no gain in generality in considering complex functionals. It may be seen directly that the real and imaginary parts

---

* The field of functions to which this representation applies is slightly extended by Fréchet, *Transactions of the American Mathematical Society*, vol. 5 (1904), p. 493. Conditions of convergence are also investigated.

of such complex functionals are real linear functionals satisfying similar conditions, and if they are real linear functionals of complex arguments, they are real linear functionals of real arguments.

Hadamard's representation is as follows:[*]

THEOREM. *The linear continuous functional T may be written in the form*

$$(8) \qquad T[\varphi(\overset{b}{\underset{a}{x}})] = \lim_{\mu = \infty} \int_a^b \varphi(x) \Psi(x, \mu) dx,$$

where for a given value of μ the function $\Psi(x, \mu)$ is continuous in x, $a \leq x \leq b$, does not involve $\varphi(x)$, and depends merely upon the form of the operation T.

To prove this theorem we take the function[†]

$$(9) \qquad F(x) = \frac{1}{\sqrt{\pi}} e^{-x^2}$$

and form the integral

$$(10) \qquad v(x, \mu) \doteq \frac{\mu}{\sqrt{\pi}} \int_a^b \varphi(u) e^{-\mu^2(u-x)^2} du.$$

As is well known, if $\varphi(u)$ is continuous, $a \leq x \leq b$, then $v(x, \mu)$ is continuous in x throughout the same interval, for every value of μ, and for that interval approaches $\varphi(x)$ uniformly as a limit, as μ becomes infinite.

Consider now the quantity $T[v(x, \mu)]$, and in relation with it the quantity

$$(11) \qquad \Psi(u, \mu) = T\left[\frac{\mu}{\sqrt{\pi}} e^{-\mu^2(u-x)^2}\right] = T[\mu F\{\mu(u - x)\}],$$

the functional operation still having reference to its argument as a function of x, the variable u being a parameter.

We have

$$\sum_1^n \varphi(u_i) \Psi(u_i, \mu) \Delta u = T\left[\sum_1^n \varphi(u_i) \frac{\mu}{\sqrt{\pi}} e^{-\mu^2(u_i-x)^2} \Delta u\right]$$

---

[*] Sur les opérations fonctionelles, *Comptes Rendus des Sciences*, vol. 136 (1903), pp. 351–354.

[†] Instead of this particular function, which is also used in connection with the equation for the flow of heat, other functions may be taken for $F(x)$. The conditions that $F(x)$ must satisfy are given in the citation from Hadamard.

from the linearity property (6).   Moreover as n becomes infinite, the sum in the right-hand member of this last equation becomes an integral, and approaches that integral uniformly for all values of x.   Hence from the continuity property of T it follows that:

$$\int_a^b \varphi(u)\Psi(u, \mu)du = T\left[\frac{\mu}{\sqrt{\pi}}\int_a^b \varphi(u)e^{-\mu^2(u-x)^2}du\right.$$
$$= T[v(x, \mu)].$$

But since $v(x, \mu)$ approaches $\varphi(x)$ uniformly, this gives us

$$(12) \qquad T[\underset{a}{\overset{b}{\varphi(x)}}] = \lim_{\mu=\infty}\int_a^b \varphi(u)\Psi(u, \mu)du,$$

where $\Psi(u, \mu)$ depends merely on the form of T and does not involve φ.

In particular, if we take for $\varphi(x)$ the function

$$\frac{\mu'}{\sqrt{\pi}}e^{-\mu'^2(u-x)^2}$$

we get an identity which is satisfied by the function $\Psi(u, \mu')$, namely

$$(12') \qquad \Psi(u, \mu') = \lim_{\mu=\infty}\frac{\mu'}{\sqrt{\pi}}\int_a^b e^{-\mu'^2(u-x)^2}\Psi(x, \mu)dx,$$

which may also be written in the form

$$(12'') \quad \lim_{\mu=\infty}\frac{\mu}{\sqrt{\pi}}\int_a^b \Psi(x, \mu')e^{-\mu^2(x-u)^2}dx$$
$$= \lim_{\mu=\infty}\frac{\mu'}{\sqrt{\pi}}\int_a^b e^{-\mu'^2(u-x)^2}\Psi(x, \mu)dx.$$

38. The Stieltjes Integral.   The theory of the Stieltjes integral is based upon the properties of *functions of finite variation*; i. e., functions $\alpha(x)$ such that if we divide up the given interval ab by points $x_0 = a, x_1, \cdots, x_n, x_{n+1} = b$, arbitrarily spaced, the sum

$$(13) \qquad \sum_{i=0}^n |\alpha(x_{i+1}) - \alpha(x_i)|$$

for the given function $\alpha(x)$ remains finite, irrespective of the value of n. A function of finite variation may be written as the difference of two non-decreasing functions

$$(13') \qquad\qquad \alpha(x) = p(x) - n(x),$$

in which, for definiteness, we write $p(a) = \alpha(a)$. If $p(x)$ and $n(x)$ are, for each value of x, the least possible functions so definable, the function

$$(14) \qquad\qquad t(x) = p(x) - p(a) + n(x)$$

is called the *total variation* of $\alpha(x)$, and is the upper limit of the sum (13) formed for the interval ax, instead of the interval ab.

We may if we like in (13') replace the two non-decreasing functions by functions which actually increase without remaining constant in any interval, although for these functions the equation (14) will no longer hold.

On account of (13') it is immediately seen that the discontinuities which a function of finite variation may have are limited in nature. In fact if x' is a point of discontinuity of $\alpha(x)$, both of the limits $\alpha(x' + 0)$ and $\alpha(x' - 0)$ must exist if x' is an interior point of the interval, and one of them, if x' is an end point of the interval. Moreover, *the number of these so-called discontinuities of the first kind is restricted*; they must be denumerable, though not necessarily countable in some preassigned order, say from left to right.

The number of intervals through which a function may remain constant is restricted in the same way.

By means of a function $\varphi(x)$ which is continuous, and a function $\alpha(x)$ which is of finite variation, in the interval $a \leq x \leq b$, form the expression

$$(15) \qquad\qquad \sum_{1}^{n+1} {}_i\varphi(\xi_i)\{\alpha(x_i) - \alpha(x_{i-1})\},$$

where the points x_i are the same as before, and the points ξ_i are arbitrary also except for the restrictions $x_{i-1} \leq \xi_i \leq x_i$. The expression (15) approaches a limit as n becomes infinite, and the maximum sub-interval approaches zero; this limit is called the *Stieltjes integral* and written

(15') $$\int_a^b \varphi(x)d\alpha(x).$$

The importance of this integral depends upon the ease with which it may be handled, and the directness of its geometric interpretation.

It is not difficult to obtain a measure of convergence of the integral. If $\psi(x)$ is a function such that $|\varphi(x)| \leq \psi(x)$, and if $p(x)$ is a non-decreasing function, we have obviously:

$$\left| \int_a^b \varphi(x)dp(x) \right| \leq \int_a^b |\varphi(x)|dp(x) \leq \int_a^b \psi(x)dp(x).$$

Also,

$$\left| \int_a^b \varphi(x)d\alpha(x) - \sum_1^{n+1}{}_i\varphi(\xi_i)\{\alpha(x_i) - \alpha(x_{i-1})\} \right|$$

$$= \left| \sum_1^{n+1}{}_i \left[\int_{x_{i-1}}^{x_i} \varphi(x)dp(x) - \varphi(\xi_i)\{p(x_i) - p(x_{i-1})\} \right. \right.$$

$$\left. \left. - \int_{x_{i-1}}^{x_i} \varphi(x)dn(x) - \varphi(\xi_i)\{n(x_i) - n(x_{i-1})\} \right| \right.$$

and by the above inequality, this expression is

$$\leq \omega_\delta \sum_1^{n+1}{}_i\{p(x_i) - p(x_{i-1}) + n(x_i) - n(x_{i-1})\},$$

where δ is the maximum length of any sub-interval, and ω_δ is the maximum oscillation of $\varphi(x)$ in any sub-interval. *Hence we have the inequality*

(16) $$\left| \int_a^b \varphi(x)d\alpha(x) - \sum_1^{n+1}{}_i\varphi(\xi_i)\{\alpha(x_i) - \alpha(x_{i-1})\} \right| \leq \omega_\delta t(b),$$

in which $t(x)$ represents the total variation of $\alpha(x)$, as a measure of the convergence of the sum (15) *to the integral* (15').

39. Regular and Irregular Parts of the Stieltjes Integral. Consider the integral

$$\int_a^b \varphi(x)dR(x),$$

in which $R(x)$ is an absolutely continuous function of x. We may write

$$R(x) - R(a) = \int_a^x r(x)dx,$$

where $r(x)$ is the derivative of $R(x)$ and is summable.

Under these conditions we have the equation

$$(17) \qquad \int_a^b \varphi(x)dR(x) = \int_a^b \varphi(x)r(x)dx$$

the integral in the right-hand member being taken in the sense of Lebesgue.

To prove this theorem, we make use of the definition of a Stieltjes integral, and write:

$$\int_a^b \varphi(x)d\int_a^x r(x)dx = \lim_{n=\infty} \sum_1^{n+1} {}_i\varphi(\xi_i) \int_{x_{i-1}}^{x_i} r(x)dx = \lim_{n=\infty} \int_a^b \varphi_n(x)r(x)dx,$$

where $\varphi_n(x) = \varphi(\xi_i)$, $x_{i-1} \leqq x < x_i$, and where therefore $\lim_{n=\infty} \varphi_n(x) = \varphi(x)$ uniformly. We now introduce the theorem:[*]

If the sequence of summable functions $\{f_n(x)\}$ converges as n becomes infinite to a function $f(x)$, and there is a positive summable function $\psi(x)$ which is at least as great as each $|f_n(x)|$, then $f(x)$ will itself be summable, and we shall have the equation:

$$\int_{x_1}^{x_2} f(x)dx = \lim_{n=\infty} \int_{x_1}^{x_2} f_n(x)dx.$$

We take

$$f_n(x) = \varphi_n(x)r(x), \qquad f(x) = \varphi(x)r(x)$$

and notice the inequality

$$|f_n(x)| \leqq \max_a^b |\varphi(x)| |r(x)|,$$

in which the right-hand member denotes a summable function. Hence we have the equation

$$\lim_{n=\infty} \int_a^b \varphi_n(x)r(x)dx = \int_a^b \varphi(x)r(x)dx,$$

and the theorem is proved.

Fréchet has given a representation of the integral (15′), in the general case, in terms of a series of discrete terms involving the function $\varphi(x)$ at special points, a Lebesgue integral, and a particular Stieltjes integral involving a function which has a vanishing derivative except at points of a set of measure zero.[†] The representation is as follows:

THEOREM. *We have*

$$(18) \qquad \int_a^b \varphi(x)d\alpha(x) = \sum_{a \leqq x_n \leqq b} A_n\varphi(x_n) + \int_a^b \varphi(x)\beta(x)dx + \int_a^b \varphi(x)d\lambda(x),$$

where A_n is the jump of $\alpha(x)$ at the point of discontinuity x_n, $\beta(x)$ is the derivative of the function $\alpha(x) - \alpha_1(x)$, $\alpha_1(x)$ being given by the definition:

$$\alpha_1(x) = \sum_{a < x_n \leqq x} \{\alpha(x_n) - \alpha(x_n - 0)\} + \sum_{a \leqq x_n < x} \{\alpha(x_n + 0) - \alpha(x_n)\},$$

$$a < x \leqq b$$

$$\alpha_1(a) = 0,$$

* De la Vallée-Poussin, *Transactions of the American Mathematical Society*, vol. 16 (1915), p. 447.

† Fréchet, *Comptes rendus du Congrès des Sociétés Savantes tenu à Grenoble* (1913), also *Transactions of the American Mathematical Society*, vol. 15 (1914), p. 152.

and $\lambda(x)$ equals $\alpha(x) - \alpha_1(x) - \int_a^x \beta(x)dx$, *a continuous function of finite variation which has a null derivative everywhere except at the points of a set of measure zero.*

It may be seen without difficulty that the representation is essentially unique.

In this theorem, the function $\alpha_1(x)$ is called the function of discontinuities. Its discontinuities are precisely the quantities

$$A_n = \alpha(x_n + 0) - \alpha(x_n - 0)$$

and its contribution to the Stieltjes integral constitutes, as may be briefly verified, the first term of the expansion (18). The summation is understood to extend over all the discontinuities x_n indicated, even though these values of x may not be denumerable in the usual order. For $x = a$ no values x_n are included in either summation, and the definition of $\alpha_1(a)$ is therefore necessary.

40. Representation of a Linear Functional by a Stieltjes Integral. We may now state the representation given by F. Riesz:

THEOREM. *The linear continuous functional $T[\varphi]$ may be written in the form*:

$$(19) \qquad T[\varphi(x)] = \int_a^b \varphi(x)d\alpha(x),$$

where $\alpha(x)$ is a function of finite variation, depending upon the form of T, but independent of $\varphi(x)$.

In order to build up the integral (19) it is desirable to extend the field of functions to which the operation T applies. We consider a set of continuous functions $\{f_n(x)\}$, such that for every value of x in ab we have

$$f_1(x) \leqq f_2(x) \leqq f_3(x) \cdots,$$

and such that for every value of x in ab the quantity

$$\varphi(x) = \lim_{n=\infty} f_n(x)$$

exists. We can show immediately from (7), by considering the absolute convergence of the series

$$T[f_1] + (T[f_2] - T[f_1]) + (T[f_3] - T[f_2]) + \cdots,$$

that $\lim_{n=\infty} T[f_n]$ exists, and we define

$$(20) \qquad T[\varphi] = \lim_{n=\infty} T[f_n].$$

It is necessary to show that this limit is independent of the choice of the sequence of functions f_n which approach φ.

Let the functions f_n and g_n form two such sequences, and consider with them the sequences $\bar{f}_n = f_n - 1/n$ and $\bar{g}_n = g_n - 1/n$. We have, since $f_n \leq f_{n+1}$ and $g_n \leq g_{n+1}$, the inequalities $\bar{f}_n < \bar{f}_{n+1}$, $\bar{g}_n < \bar{g}_{n+1}$, and also, as follows by an obvious calculation:

$$\lim_{n=\infty} T[\bar{f}_n] = \lim_{n=\infty} T[f_n], \qquad \lim_{n=\infty} T[\bar{g}_n] = \lim_{n=\infty} T[g_n].$$

Given $\bar{f}_m$ we can take n great enough so that $\bar{g}_n > \bar{f}_m$. In fact, since $\bar{f}_m$ and $\bar{g}_n$ are continuous functions of x, the values of x for which $\bar{g}_n \leq \bar{f}_m$ form a closed set E_n, and $E_{n'}$ is included in E_n if $n' > n$. Hence if we cannot find n great enough so that there are no points in E_n, there will be a point x_0 such that*

$$\lim_{n=\infty} \bar{g}_n(x_0) \leq \bar{f}_m(x_0),$$

which is a contradiction, since $\bar{f}_m(x_0) < \varphi(x_0)$.

We can then form a sequence of functions $\bar{f}_{m_1}(x) < \bar{g}_{m_1}(x) < \bar{f}_{m_2}(x) < \bar{g}_{m_2}(x) \cdots$, approaching $\varphi(x)$ as a limit. If we form the functional T for this sequence, it will approach a limit which cannot be different from $\lim_{n=\infty} T[\bar{f}_n]$ or $\lim_{n=\infty} T[\bar{g}_n]$ and will therefore be the functional $T[\varphi]$ already defined.

The functional T is linear in these functions, i. e.,

$$T[c_1\varphi_1 + c_2\varphi_2] = c_1 T[\varphi_1] + c_2 T[\varphi_2]$$

if c_1 and c_2 are restricted to positive constants. In order to make T completely distributive we need to define

$$(21) \qquad T[\varphi_1 - \varphi_2] = T[\varphi_1] - \cdot T[\varphi_2],$$

a definition whose uniqueness is directly verifiable. We should however prove also the inequality (7):

$$|T[\varphi_1 - \varphi_2]| \leq M \max_a^b |\varphi_1 - \varphi_2|.$$

---

* If we have a sequence of point sets, each contained in the preceding, and none of them a null set, then there will be a point common to all of them, provided they are all closed sets.

Let us denote max $|\varphi_1 - \varphi_2|$ by G, and let f_n and g_n be two sequences which have as limits φ_1 and φ_2 respectively.　Define a new function h_n as follows:

$$h_n(x) = f_n(x) \qquad \text{wherever} \qquad |f_n(x) - g_n(x)| \leq G,$$

$$(22) \quad h_n(x) = g_n(x) + G \qquad \text{wherever} \qquad f_n - g_n > G,$$

$$h_n(x) = g_n(x) - G \qquad \text{wherever} \qquad g_n - f_n > G.$$

By this definition we have, as may be directly verified,

$$h_{n+1}(x) \geq h_n(x)$$

and also

$$\lim_{n=\infty} h_n(x) = \varphi_1(x).$$

We have however by the definition (21):

$$|T[\varphi_1 - \varphi_2]| = \lim_{n=\infty} |T[f_n] - T[g_n]|$$

$$= \lim_{n=\infty} |T[h_n - g_n]|$$

which by (22) is $\leq MG$.

Our field as now extended is such that if $\varphi_1, \cdots, \varphi_k$ belong to it, any linear combination of them will belong to it, and will satisfy the inequality (7).　With this, we are in a position to construct the Stieltjes integral.

The function which is unity in the sub-interval $c < x < h$, and zero otherwise, is the limit of a sequence of continuous functions $f_n(x)$, increasing with n.　Hence the function

$$(23) \quad \begin{aligned} f_{cd} &= 1, \qquad c < x \leq d \qquad (c > a), \\ &= 0, \qquad \text{otherwise,} \end{aligned}$$

is the difference of two such functions, and therefore a member of the field of definition of the functional T.　The function which we denote by f_{ad} and define as:

$$(23') \quad \begin{aligned} f_{ad} &= 1, \qquad a \leq x \leq d, \\ &= 0, \qquad \text{otherwise,} \end{aligned}$$

is the limit of a decreasing sequence, and is also of the field of T.

The function $\alpha(x)$ defined by the equations

(24)
$$\alpha(a) = 0,$$
$$\alpha(x) = T[f_{ax}], \qquad x \neq a,$$

is a function of limited variation; for, from the equation

$$\sum_{1}^{n+1}{}_i |\alpha(x_i) - \alpha(x_{i-1})| = \sum_{1}^{n} |T[f_{x_{i-1}x_i}]|$$

and the inequality (7), it follows that

$$\sum_{1}^{n+1}{}_i |\alpha(x_i) - \alpha(x_{i-1})| \leq M.$$

In order to form $T[\varphi(x)]$ we build up the continuous function $\varphi(x)$ out of the functions f_{cd}, and define

$$\varphi_n(x) = \sum_{1}^{n+1} \varphi(\xi_i) f_{x_{i-1}x_i}(x),$$

which is a member of the field of T, and approaches $\varphi(x)$ uniformly as n becomes infinite, for $a \leq x \leq b$. Hence

$$T[\varphi(x)] = \lim_{n=\infty} T[\varphi_n(x)].$$

But

$$T[\varphi_n] = \sum_{1}^{n+1}{}_i \varphi(\xi_i)[\alpha(x_i) - \alpha(x_{i-1})],$$

and therefore, from the definition of a Stieltjes integral, we get (19).

41. Representation of $T[\varphi]$ as a Lebesgue Integral. Not only is it possible to split up the Stieltjes integral into three parts, of which the middle term is a Lebesgue integral of simple form, but also, as Lebesgue himself has shown, the Stieltjes integral can as a whole be replaced by a single Lebesgue integral, thus getting an essentially new representation of the linear functional. Although the representation loses in directness, it gains in the extension of the field of functions to which it may be applied.

In order to make this transformation it is necessary to make a change of independent variable which will smooth out the discontinuities in $\alpha(x)$, leaving it everywhere the integral of its derivative function. And in removing the discontinuities, gaps are created which it is necessary to fill by more or less artificial definitions of the functions involved in the integrand.

Following Lebesgue we make the transformation

$$t = t(x),$$

where $t(x)$ is the total variation function of $\alpha(x)$. In order to make the inverse of this function single valued, we must make a special definition of $x(t)$ in the intervals where $\alpha(x)$, and therefore $t(x)$, is constant. If $t(x)$ has the value t_0 in an interval lm, we take as $x(t_0)$, only one of the values in lm, say l, the least value. We thus make $\varphi(x(t))$ discontinuous at a denumerable infinity of points.

If $t(x)$ is discontinuous for a certain value of x, say $x = x_n$, $x(t)$ will not be defined in the interval $\{t(x_n - 0),\ t(x_n + 0)\}$ except for the value $t(x_n)$. Throughout the whole of this interval we write

$$x(t) = x_n$$
$$\varphi(x(t)) = \varphi(x_n),$$

and define $\alpha(x(t))$ as a linear function of t in the partial intervals

$$\{t(x_n - 0),\ t(x_n)\}, \qquad \{t(x_n),\ t(x_n + 0)\},$$

thus obtaining a continuous function $\gamma(t)$ of t, for which

$$(25) \qquad \int_a^b \varphi(x)d\alpha(x) = \int_0^{t(b)} \varphi(x(t))d\gamma(t),$$

as a direct inspection of the limiting sums will show.*

The function $\gamma(t)$ is still a function of limited variation, and possesses therefore a finite derivative $\theta(t)$, except at the points of a set of zero measure, integrable in the Lebesgue sense, considered at the points where it is finite. Moreover the total variation of $\gamma(t)$ in an interval 0 is t itself, and therefore $\gamma(t)$ is an absolutely continuous function of t. Hence it is itself the integral of $\theta(t)$,

$$\int_0^t \theta(t)dt = \gamma(t),$$

and an application of the first theorem of Art. 39 yields the result

$$(26) \qquad \int_0^{t(b)} \varphi(x(t))d\gamma(t) = \int_0^{t(b)} \varphi(x(t))\theta(t)dt.$$

The function $\theta(t)$ takes on merely the values $+ 1$ and $- 1$.

We have then Lebesgue's result:

THEOREM. *The linear continuous functional $T[\varphi]$ may be written in the form*

$$(27) \qquad T[\varphi(\overset{b}{\underset{a}{x}})] = \int_0^{t(b)} \varphi(x(t))\theta(t)dt,$$

where $x(t)$ and $\theta(t)$ are functions depending only on the form of T, but independent of the argument φ. The function $\theta(t)$ takes on merely the values $+ 1$ and $- 1$, and $x(t)$ is a non-decreasing, but not necessarily continuous function of t.

The transformation, just described, may be carried through in various ways, such as by writing $\alpha(x)$ as the difference of two non-decreasing functions. More general transformations of this kind exist which have no special reference

---

* This involves, on account of the discontinuities of $\varphi(x(t))$, a slight, but obvious extension of the definition of the Stieltjes integral, $\gamma(t)$ being continuous.

to a function of finite variation, but deal with the parametric representation of a continuous curve.*

In this respect, the present case corresponds to that where the curve is rectifiable.

The equation (27) provides for a further generalization of the linear operation T. We have already seen, in F. Riesz's representation, that if the functional T applies to all continuous functions it also applies to certain discontinuous functions which can be built up from the limits of increasing sequences of functions. Lebesgue notices that the right-hand member of (27) is defined and distributive when φ is any limited summable function, providing thus an extension of the field of definition of $T[\varphi]$; moreover that the representation has the property:

$$\lim_{n=\infty} \int_a^b \varphi_n(x(t))\theta(t)dt = \int_a^b \varphi(x(t))\theta(t)dt$$

if the functions $\varphi_n(x)$ are summable and limited in their set, and

$$\varphi(x) = \lim_{n=\infty} \varphi_n(x).$$

The equation (27) may therefore be used to provide an extension of the definition of the Stieltjes integral to the case where the integrand $\varphi(x)$ is limited and summable, an extension which however departs from the geometric interpretation.†

Direct extensions of the field and the analysis of the Stieltjes integral have been given by Radon, *Wiener Sitzungsberichte*, vol. 122 (1913), pp. 1295–1438, and by Daniell, *Bulletin of the American Mathematical Society*, vol. 23 (1917), p. 211.

§ 3. The Linear Functional for Restricted Fields

42. Continuity of Order k. In general, the more limited the field of the functional $T[\varphi]$, the more unrestricted may be the character of the operation T itself; and vice versa. We may, for instance, expect to find functionals which apply only to analytic functions. On the other hand, functionals which apply to a certain field may by definition, as we have already seen, sometimes be extended to more general fields.

We say that a functional $\Phi[\varphi]$ has continuity of order k, if, when the argument φ is continuous with its first k derivatives,

---

* Jackson, *Bulletin of the American Mathematical Society*, vol. 24 (1917), p. 77; see also Fréchet, Thèse, Note 1, *Rendiconti del Circolo Matematico di Palermo*, vol. 22 (1906), pp. 1–74.

† Integrals somewhat analogous in form to the Stieltjes integral have been treated by Hellinger, Dissertation, Göttingen (1907), Habilitationschrift, *Journal für Mathematik*, vol. 136; H. Hahn, *Monatshefte der Mathematik und Physik*, vol. 23 (1912), p. 161.

the increment of $\Phi[\varphi]$ can be made to approach zero, by making the increment of φ together with its first k derivatives approach zero uniformly and simultaneously; that is, we can make

$$|\Phi[\varphi + \theta] - \Phi[\varphi]| < \epsilon$$

by taking

$$|\theta(x)| < \eta, \cdots, |\theta^{(k)}(x)| < \eta.$$

The usual continuity is of order zero, and the forms of $T[\varphi]$ already obtained are deduced by processes valid only under this hypothesis.

A brief examination suffices to show that we cannot extend functionals which have continuity merely of order k, by definition over other fields so that they have continuity of order less than k; thus if $T[y] = dy/dx$, $T[y]$ will become infinite with dy/dx, and therefore cannot be applied to functionals which are merely the uniform limits of functions continuous with continuous first derivatives. The functionals used so extensively in Lecture I are not in general special cases of those treated in § 2.

43. The Linear Functional, Continuous of Order k. An explicit formula for a functional which has continuity merely of order k has been given lately by Fischer.* He points out that if $\varphi(x)$ is of class k it can be written in the form

$$(28) \quad \varphi(x) = \int_a^x dx_1 \int_a^{x_1} dx_2 \cdots \int_a^{x_{k-1}} \varphi^{(k)}(x_k) dx_k + \sum_{i=1}^k \frac{\varphi^{(k-i)}(a)}{(k-i)!} (x - a)^{k-i},$$

and if $T[\varphi]$ is linear it will consequently have the form:

$$(29) \quad T[\varphi] \underset{a}{\overset{b}{}} = T_k[\varphi^{(k)}(x)] \underset{a}{\overset{b}{}} + \sum_1^k \frac{\varphi^{(k-i)}(a)}{(k-i)!} T[(x - a)^{k-i}] \underset{a}{\overset{b}{}},$$

where the functional

$$T_k[\varphi^k(x)] \underset{a}{\overset{b}{}} = T \int_a^x dx_1 \cdots \int_a^{x_{k-1}} \varphi^{(k)}(x_k) dx_k]$$

---

* Fischer, *Bulletin of the American Mathematical Society*, vol. 23 (1916), pp. 88–90. An extension to functionals of surfaces is also given.

is linear and continuous of the zeroth order in its argument $\varphi^{(k)}(x)$, and the $T[(\overset{b}{x} - a)^{k-i}]$, $i = 1, 2, \cdots,$ are certain constants. Conversely, any functional of the form

$$(30) \qquad T_k[\varphi^{(k)}(x)] + \cdot \sum_1^k A_i \varphi^{(k-i)}(a) = T[\varphi(\overset{b}{x})]$$

where T_k has continuity of order zero in its argument, and the A_i are arbitrary constants, has continuity of order k. There is however no reason for preferring the point a over the point b or over any interior point.

A more natural form, obviously redundant, but possibly useful, is the following:

$$(31) \qquad T[\varphi(\overset{b}{x})] = \sum_{i=0}^k T_i[\varphi^{(i)}(\overset{b}{x})],$$

in which each of the functionals $T_i[\varphi^{(i)}(x)]$ has continuity of order zero.

An interesting form is also obtained by consideration of Hadamard's representation. By a proper choice of $\Psi(x, \mu)$ various particular functionals may be obtained with continuity of assigned order—for instance the representation of $\varphi^{(k)}(x)$. The functional represented depends upon the manner of convergence of the integral to its limit as μ becomes infinite, and what conditions must be imposed on $\varphi(x)$ to insure that convergence. It is therefore desirable to remove, if possible, the condition of continuity of order zero, which was used in the deduction of (8).

If $T[\varphi]$ has continuity merely of order k, it may be written as:

$$(32) \qquad T[\varphi(\overset{b}{x})] = \lim_{n=\infty} \int_{a-\epsilon}^{b+\epsilon} \varphi(x) P(x, n) dx,$$

where $\varphi(x)$ is extended continuously with its first k derivatives beyond the interval ab to the interval $\{a - \epsilon, b + \epsilon\}$, ϵ being a quantity arbitrarily small, and positive. For $P(u, n)$ we may take the function

$$\Psi(u, n) = T\left[\frac{n}{\sqrt{\pi}} e^{-n^2(u-x)^2} \right]$$

of Hadamard, and show that $v(x, n)$ approaches $\varphi(x)$ with its first k derivatives, as n becomes infinite, uniformly for x in ab, or we can take such a function as

$$P(u, n) = \sqrt{\frac{n}{\pi}}\ T[\{1 - (u - \overset{b}{\underset{a}{x}})^2\}^n],$$

and make use of the familiar theorems for polynomial approximation.*

§ 4. Volterra's Theorem for Implicit Functional Equations

44. The Differential of a Functional.   Form the expression

$$(33) \qquad \Delta F = F[\varphi + \Delta\varphi] - F[\varphi],$$

where the functional $F[\varphi]$ is continuous in its argument $\varphi(x)$. According to Fréchet,† the differential of F for a given φ is a linear functional $T[\Delta\varphi]$ of the arbitrary continuous increment $\Delta\varphi$ of φ, such that the inequality

$$(34) \qquad |\Delta F - T[\Delta\varphi]| < \epsilon \max_a^b |\Delta\varphi|$$

is satisfied.   The quantity ϵ in (34) is assumed to approach zero with $\max |\Delta\varphi|$.

If for a given function φ no linear functional $T[\Delta\varphi]$ can be found to satisfy (34), $F[\varphi]$ does not have a differential for the function φ.   From (34) and the linearity of T, it follows that T must be a continuous functional of its argument $\Delta\varphi$.   Hence $T[\Delta\varphi]$ must be expressible in terms of the formulæ developed in § 2.‡   We shall consider in what follows only particular cases of those general expressions.

* De la Vallée-Poussin, Traité d'analyse infinitésimale, vol. II, Paris (1912), p. 132.

† *Transactions of the American Mathematical Society*, vol. 15 (1914), p. 139.

‡ If $F[\varphi]$ has continuity merely of order k, we restrict $\Delta\varphi$ to functions which approach zero uniformly, together with their first k derivatives.   It follows that the linear functional $T[\Delta\varphi]$ has continuity of order k, and it will therefore be expressible according to the formulæ of § 3.

45. Volterra's Theorem. Volterra considers the functional equation

$$(35) \qquad H[\varphi(\overset{b}{\underset{a}{s}}),\ f(\overset{b}{\underset{a}{s}})\,|\,x] = 0,$$

in which the left-hand member is continuous in its three arguments, namely, the functions φ and ψ and the parameter x; the equation is assumed to be satisfied by the function $\varphi(x) = 0$, when $f(x)$ is itself put identically equal to zero, and the problem is to determine $\varphi(x)$ in terms of $f(x)$ in the functional neighborhood of $f = 0$, $\varphi = 0$, that is, in the neighborhood $|f(x)| < N$, $|\varphi(x)| < N$, N small enough.

To take the definite case considered by Volterra, let the differential of H due to a change of φ alone be given by the special formula

$$(36) \qquad d_\phi H = \Delta\varphi(x) - \int_a^b H_\phi[\varphi(\overset{b}{\underset{a}{s}}),\ f(\overset{b}{\underset{u}{s}})\,|\,x,\ x']\Delta\varphi(x')dx',$$

where

$$(37) \qquad |\Delta_\phi H - d_\phi H| < \epsilon \max_a^b |\Delta\varphi(x)|,$$

and $H_\phi[\varphi, f\,|\,x, x']$ is limited and continuous with respect to its four arguments; and let (36) take on the form

$$(38) \qquad d_\phi H = \Delta\varphi(x) - \int_a^b G(xx')\Delta\varphi(x')dx',$$

when f and φ are made to vanish identically.

THEOREM.   *In the given neighborhood for φ and f, and the given interval for x, let $H[\varphi, f\,|\,x]$ have a differential of form (36) where*

(i) the quantity ϵ in (37) approaches zero with $\max |\varphi(x)|$ uniformly for all functions φ, f and all values x in the domain considered, and

(ii) the Fredholm determinant of the kernel $G(xx')$ in (38) is unequal to zero.*

Then there is a neighborhood of $f = 0$, $\varphi = 0$, namely, $\{\,|f| \leq N'$, $|\varphi| \leq N'\}$, N' some value $\leq N$, in which (35) has one and only one solution $\varphi(x)$ for a given continuous function $f(x)$.

The proof of this theorem is not difficult.   Write (35) in the form

---

* That is, unity is not a characteristic value for the kernel $G(x, x')$.

$$\text{(39)} \quad \begin{aligned} \varphi(x) &- \int_a^b G(xx')\varphi(x')dx' \\ &= \varphi(x) - \int_a^b G(xx')\varphi(x')dx' - H[\varphi, f\,|\,x] \end{aligned}$$

and denote the right-hand member by $\Theta[\varphi, f\,|\,x]$. The differential of Θ,

$$\text{(39')} \quad d_\phi\Theta[\varphi, f\,|\,x] = -\int_a^b \{G(xx') - H_\phi[\varphi, f\,|\,xx']\}\Delta\varphi(x')dx',$$

may be written for brevity in the form

$$\int_a^b R[\varphi, f\,|\,xx']\Delta\varphi(x')dx',$$

and satisfies the inequality

$$|\Delta_\phi\Theta - d_\phi\Theta| < \epsilon \max_a^b |\Delta\varphi(x)|,$$

where the ϵ is the ϵ of (37).

Equation (39) may be taken as an integral equation in $\varphi(x)$, the right-hand member being regarded for the moment as a known function of x. It yields then the result

$$\text{(40)} \quad \varphi(x) = \Phi[\varphi, f\,|\,x]$$

where

$$\text{(40')} \quad \Phi[\varphi, f\,|\,x] = \Theta[\varphi, f\,|\,x] - \int_a^b \Gamma(xx')\Theta[\varphi, f\,|\,x']dx',$$

and $\Gamma(xx')$ is the kernel resolvent for $G(xx')$. Moreover, we can deduce (39) from (40) by the resolution of the inverse integral equation, so that (39) and (40) are fully equivalent. Equation (40) is however of the form of (1) Art. 1, and satisfies the conditions there imposed.

We have in fact for $d_\phi\Phi$ the formula

$$\text{(41)} \quad \begin{aligned} d_\phi\Phi = \int_a^b dx'\Delta\varphi(x')\{R[\varphi, f\,|\,xx'] \\ - \int_a^b \Gamma(x, x'')R[\varphi, f\,|\,x''x']dx''\} \end{aligned}$$

and for $\Delta_\phi\Phi$ the inequality

$$|\Delta_\phi\Phi - d_\phi\Phi| < \epsilon \max_a^b |\Delta\varphi(x)|\{1 + \int_a^b |\Gamma(xx')|dx'\},$$

since Φ is itself linear in Θ.   This yields the inequality

$$(41') \qquad |\Delta_\phi\Phi - d_\phi\Phi| < \eta \max_a^b |\Delta\varphi(x)|,$$

where η approaches zero with $\max |\Delta\varphi(x)|$, uniformly for all functions φ, f and all values x in the domain considered.

The functional $R[\varphi, f | xx']$ can be made uniformly as small as we please by restricting φ and f to a neighborhood (say $< M'$) small enough; and therefore by taking a proper value of M', the restriction

$$|R[\varphi f | xx']| + \int_a^b |\Gamma(xx'')R[\varphi f | x''x']| \, dx' < \frac{r}{b-a}$$

will hold, where r is given arbitrarily in advance, and this, with the aid of (41) and (41'), yields the inequality

$$(42) \qquad \Delta_\phi\Phi < (r + \eta) \max_a^b |\Delta\varphi(x)|.$$

Let M'' be small enough so that if $\max |\Delta\varphi| \leq M''$, η will be less than $\frac{1}{2}$, let M' be small enough so that $r < \frac{1}{2}$, and take N'' as the smaller of the two numbers M', $M''/2$ (so that if $|\varphi_1|$ and $|\varphi_2|$ are $< N''$, their difference may be less than M'').

For a given function $f(x)$, the class L of the theorem of Art. 1 is defined as the totality of continuous functions $\varphi(x)$ for which

$$(42'') \qquad |\varphi(x) - \Phi[0, f | x]| \leq N''.$$

In virtue of (42), since $r + \eta < 1$, both (i) and (ii) of Art. 1 will be satisfied, and there will be one and only one continuous function $\varphi(x)$ which for a given $f(x)$ satisfies the equation (35).

If we introduce N', taking $N' < N''/2$, the neighborhood specified in the enunciation of Volterra's theorem will be such that (42'') is satisfied, and the theorem will be proved.

This is not of course the only possible theorem on the solution of implicit functional equations.   More general theorems may be obtained, and other particular theorems also, depending upon what form we assume for the quantity $d_\phi H$ in (36), and what the solution of the resulting linear integral equation may be.*

* Certain forms of these linear equations are considered in Lecture V.

LECTURE IV

INTEGRO–DIFFERENTIAL EQUATIONS OF THE BÔCHER TYPE*

§ 1. The Generalization of Laplace's Equation

46. Hypothetical Experiments as a Basis of Physics. It is regarded as experimental knowledge that in a dielectric the field of force due to electric charges, distributed arbitrarily, is conservative; and also that the total electric induction over a closed surface in a dielectric is 4π multiplied into the charge of electricity inside the surface. In what sense are these laws experimental? Obviously no experiment has ever yet been performed in which the total work was null; and no measurements upon total induction could be taken with such accuracy as to fix the multiplicative factor absolutely as 4π, or even to show that it was constant.

And yet these laws are not entirely the results of more general laws of nature, nor are they implied wholly in definitions of such things as "charge," "dielectric," etc. It was only after Coulomb had made his direct (and inaccurate) experiments that he was able to state the proposition: that two point charges m and m' repel each other with a force mm'/r^2. At least in some way therefore, although there are no such things as point charges, Coulomb's law is an experimental law.

The characteristic terms of physics—point charges, electric density, dielectrics, conductors,—are as ideal as the points, lines, and numbers of pure mathematics. The basic laws of any branch of physics are stated as hypothetical experiments carried out upon these ideal elements; e. g., "if two point charges are at

---

* This lecture is based on the following references:

M. Bôcher, On harmonic functions in two dimensions, *Proceedings of the American Academy of Science*, vol. 41 (1905–06).

G. C. Evans, On the reduction of integro-differential equations, *Transactions of the American Mathematical Society*, vol. 15 (1914), pp. 477–496;

Sul calcolo della funzione di Green, *Rendiconti della R. Accademia dei Lincei*, vol. 22 (1913), first semester, pp. 855–860.

C. W. Oseen, Über die Bedeutung der Integralgleichungen in der Theorie der Bewegung einer reibenden, unzusammendrückbaren Flüssigkeit, *Arkiv för Matematik, Astronomi och Fysik*, 6 (1911), No. 23. Here an extension of the corresponding Green's theorem is given.

distance r and have masses of electricity m and m', they will repel each other with a force mm'/r^2." The characteristic elements are suggested by approximately invariant processes in phenomena, and the postulates which frame the hypothetical experiments are arrived at by a process of successive approximation in the carrying out of actual experiments: "If charges of masses m and m' are concentrated on smaller and smaller pith balls, the force of repulsion can be made as near mm'/r^2 as the accuracy of measurement will allow." This is the same sort of experimentation which justifies the postulate of parallels, and distinguishes between Euclidean and Non-euclidean spaces, as far at least as this distinction, even in actual space, is not a matter of the definition of characteristic elements.

In order to make satisfactory any branch of theoretical physics, the basic elements should be chosen, and hypothetical experiments given in scope sufficient to determine completely the properties of those elements. The results of these experiments, stated as postulates, should be sufficient to develop, by their logical combination, all the details of the subject. In other words, *in the mathematical treatment of the subject there should be no new elements introduced, or new properties made use of*.

In some cases, this general proposition suggests an immediate modification of the existing theory. To take an example, in the theory of electricity, the potential and its first derivatives correspond to possible physical elements, namely, work and force; also certain differential parameters of the second order, such as the Laplacian of the potential, have physical interpretation in terms of electric density, etc.; but in order to introduce the second partial derivatives, by themselves, we must make new hypotheses sufficient to insure their existence. These hypotheses, however, are not the results of hypothetical experiments and have apparently no physical meaning inherent in the subject itself. To show the existence of the second derivative of $\int\int\int f/r\,dxdydz$ it is necessary to demand more than the mere integrability, or even continuity, of $f(xyz)$.

This difficulty disappears if instead of considering the differential equations, which are the results of limiting processes and involve assumptions about the existence of the limits, we consider the equations which express in integral form the results of our experiments. Thus, the equations

$$(1) \qquad \int_c \varphi_s ds = 0,$$

$$(2) \qquad \int\int \varphi_n d\sigma = \int\int\int f(xyz) dS,$$

φ being a vector point function, represent the postulate of a conservative field of force, and the law of total induction in a medium of inductivity unity. The usual process is to pass from (1) and (2) to the consideration of Poisson's equation.

47. Bôcher's Treatment of Laplace's Equation. Professor Bôcher considers the relation

$$(3) \qquad \int_c \frac{\partial u(xy)}{\partial n} ds = 0,$$

assumed to hold merely for all circles within a given two dimensional region, and shows that when we assume merely the existence and continuity of u and its first derivatives, the equation is nevertheless entirely equivalent to Laplace's equation provided that the region is restricted to that of the customary analysis (that is, one in which analytic continuation is possible; called by Borel, a Weierstrass region). By means of a two-way evaluation of the double integral

$$(3') \qquad \int\int \frac{1}{r}\frac{\partial u}{\partial r} d\sigma = \int\int \frac{\partial u}{\partial r} dr d\theta$$

extended over the interior of the circle, we can pass directly from (3) to the mean value theorem*

$$(3'') \qquad u_0 = \frac{1}{2\pi}\int_0^{2\pi} u d\theta.$$

In this way the uniqueness of the solution of (3) for given continuous boundary values on a closed curve is easily established.

---

* Bôcher, *Bulletin of the American Mathematical Society*, (2), 1 (1895), p. 205.

In fact, suppose that $u_1(xy)$ and $u_2(xy)$ were two functions which on the regular boundary of a simply connected region took on continuously the same values $h(M)$, and satisfied, for every circle contained within that region, the equation (3). Then their difference would also satisfy (3), and take on zero values on the boundary. This would imply, if the difference were not identically zero, that at some point P, in the interior, it would have a positive maximum or a negative minimum value. But if this point P were surrounded by a circle small enough to lie entirely within the region, the value at P would not be the mean of the values on the circumference. Therefore the value of the difference must be identically zero.

On the other hand, as is well known, there is a harmonic function $\bar{u}(x, y)$ which takes on the given boundary values $h(M)$; since it is harmonic, however, it satisfies the equation (3). The unique solution of (3) must therefore be harmonic: its second derivatives must exist at all interior points, and the equation

$$\frac{\partial^2 u}{\partial x^2} + \frac{\partial^2 u}{\partial y^2} = 0$$

must be satisfied. The equation (3), then, throughout regions in which u, $\partial u/\partial x$ and $\partial u/\partial y$ are continuous defines the same class of functions as that defined by Laplace's equation.

I have called equations of the type of (3) *integro-differential equations of Bôcher type*. This lecture is devoted to the treatment of the general equation of that type involving derivatives of the first order, corresponding therefore to the general linear partial differential equation of the second order: in the general equation, unlike the case of (3), the second derivatives will not even exist.

48. Poisson's Equation. If we write down the equations (1) and (2) for two dimensions, the first one tells us that there is a function

(4) $$u(xy) = \int_{(x_0 y_0)}^{(x,\,y)} \varphi_s ds$$

such that $\partial u/\partial s$ is φ_s. The second equation thereupon gives us the relation

(5)
$$\int_c \frac{\partial u}{\partial n} ds = \int \int f(xy) dx dy$$

for an arbitrary contour C in the given region. Equation (5) corresponds to Poisson's equation

(6)
$$\frac{\partial^2 u}{\partial x^2} + \frac{\partial^2 u}{\partial y^2} = -f(xy).$$

The latter has in general no solution if $f(xy)$ is merely continuous; the former however has one, and it is uniquely determined by given continuous boundary values. The uniqueness of the solution comes from the fact that the difference of two solutions of (5) is a solution of (3). The existence of the solution is demonstrated by showing that the function

$$\frac{1}{2\pi} \int \int g(xy \,|\, x'y') f(x'y') dx' dy'$$

where $g(xy \,|\, x'y')$ represents the usual Green's function for Laplace's equation, satisfies (5) and takes on null boundary values. This function then, plus the harmonic function which takes on the desired boundary values, will be the desired unique solution of (5).

The equation (5), and the corresponding equation for three dimensions

(7)
$$\int \int \frac{\partial u}{\partial n} d\sigma = \int \int \int f(xyz) dx dy dz,$$

may also be treated by a direct generalization of Bôcher's method of double integration, considering orthogonal systems of curves, and the expression of the integral in curvilinear co-ordinates, in case we do not restrict the closed surfaces of integration in (7) to spheres. The integration over the enclosed volume may be expressed as the iteration of a surface and a simple integral, and performed in two ways. In the case where spheres are used the element of surface integration is the solid angle; in the case where the closed surface in (7) is unrestricted, the element of surface integration is a functional of closed curves on that surface which bears to the function $\varphi(xyz) = c$, which defines the family of surfaces corresponding to the concentric spheres, a relation which is the generalization of the relation, in two dimensions, between a harmonic function and its conjugate; viz., the flux of the functional is the gradient of φ. This relation, holding between a harmonic function, which defines a family of isothermal surfaces, and a certain functional of curves on those surfaces, has been treated in a different connection by Volterra.* It has nothing to do with the relation between the real and imaginary parts of the functionals of Lecture II, although it is in one direction a generalization of the properties of analytic functions.

Rather than follow through this analysis we shall turn to the more generally applicable method of Green's theorem.

§ 2. Green's Theorem for the General Linear Integro-Differential Equation of Bôcher Type

49. Adjoint Integro-Differential Equations. We shall consider the integro-differential expression

$$(8) \quad \Lambda[C, u_s] = \int_C \left\{ \alpha_{11} \frac{\partial u}{\partial x} + \alpha_{12} \frac{\partial u}{\partial y} + \alpha_1 u \right\} dy$$
$$- \left\{ \alpha_{21} \frac{\partial u}{\partial x} + \alpha_{22} \frac{\partial u}{\partial y} + \alpha_2 u \right\} dx,$$

and form the equation

$$(9) \quad \Lambda[C|u_s] = \int\int_\sigma (f - \alpha u) dx dy,$$

where σ is the area enclosed by C. In case derivatives of sufficient order exist of u, and of the coefficients α_{ij}, α_i, α, the equation (9) may be written as a partial differential equation; namely

$$(9') \quad a_{11} \frac{\partial^2 u}{\partial x^2} + 2a_{12} \frac{\partial^2 u}{\partial x \partial y} + a_{22} \frac{\partial^2 u}{\partial y^2} + a_1 \frac{\partial u}{\partial x} + a_2 \frac{\partial u}{\partial y} + au = f,$$

* Volterra, Leçons sur l'intégration des équations différentielles aux dérivées partielles; professées à Stockholm, Paris (Reprint 1912).

in which the coefficients are defined by the equations

$$a_{11} = \alpha_{11}, \qquad a_{22} = \alpha_{22}, \qquad 2a_{12} = \alpha_{12} + \alpha_{21},$$

$$(9'') \quad a_1 = \frac{\partial \alpha_{11}}{\partial x} + \frac{\partial \alpha_{21}}{\partial y} + \alpha_1, \qquad a_2 = \frac{\partial \alpha_{12}}{\partial x} + \frac{\partial \alpha_{22}}{\partial y} + \alpha_2,$$

$$a = \frac{\partial \alpha_1}{\partial x} + \frac{\partial \alpha_2}{\partial y} + \alpha.$$

Additional derivatives would be involved in the definition of the adjoint expression to (9'). The assumptions we shall use are, however, given below.

With (8) and (9) we consider the expression

$$(10) \quad \Gamma[C, v_s] = \int_C \left\{ \beta_{11} \frac{\partial v}{\partial x} + \beta_{12} \frac{\partial v}{\partial y} + \beta_1 v \right\} dy$$
$$- \left\{ \beta_{21} \frac{\partial v}{\partial x} + \beta_{22} \frac{\partial v}{\partial y} + \beta_2 v \right\} dx$$

and *the equation*

$$(11) \qquad \Gamma[C, v_s] = \int \int_\sigma (g - \beta v) dx dy$$

which we call the adjoint of (9), *provided that the relations*

$$(12) \qquad \begin{aligned} \beta_{ij} &= \alpha_{ji}, \qquad i, j = 1, 2, \\ \beta_i &= -\alpha_i, \qquad i = 1, 2, \end{aligned}$$

$$\beta = \alpha + \frac{\partial \alpha_1}{\partial x} + \frac{\partial \alpha_2}{\partial y},$$

are satisfied. If the last of these equations is written in the symmetrical form

$$(12') \qquad 2\alpha + \frac{\partial \alpha_1}{\partial x} + \frac{\partial \alpha_2}{\partial y} = 2\beta + \frac{\partial \beta_1}{\partial x} + \frac{\partial \beta_2}{\partial y},$$

it is seen at once that the relation between an equation and its adjoint is symmetrical: if (11) is the adjoint of (9) then (9) is the adjoint of (11).

The curve C is to be restricted to what may be called a *standard curve.* A standard curve is a closed curve which does not cut itself at any point, composed of a finite number of portions; for each portion, the co-ordinates of any point are given by two functions $\varphi(q)$ and $\psi(q)$, throughout a finite interval for a parameter q; the functions $\varphi(q)$ and $\psi(q)$ are assumed to be continuous throughout the closed interval, and therefore finite, with their derivatives of the first order. It is assumed that $\varphi'(q)$ and $\psi'(q)$ vanish only at a finite number of points unless they vanish identically, and do not both vanish at the same value of q. Hence no line parallel to either of the axes can cut the curve in more than a finite number of points, unless it includes itself a portion of the curve.

A standard curve *approaches a point P uniformly*, if, given an arbitrarily small circle with center at P, the curve comes and remains within that circle.

We consider a simply connected region Σ and assume that at every point of it, the functions u, v and their first partial derivatives, also f, g, α_{ij}, α_1, α_2, $\partial\alpha_1/\partial x$, $\partial\alpha_2/\partial y$ and α remain finite and continuous. We form the expression

$$(13) \quad H[C, u_s, v_s] = \int_C \left\{ \left[\alpha_{11}\left(v\,\frac{\partial u}{\partial x} - u\,\frac{\partial v}{\partial x} \right) \right. \right.$$
$$+ \left(\alpha_{12}v\,\frac{\partial u}{\partial y} - \alpha_{21}u\,\frac{\partial v}{\partial y} \right) + \alpha_1 uv \Big] dy$$
$$- \left[\left(\alpha_{21}v\,\frac{\partial u}{\partial x} - \alpha_{12}u\,\frac{\partial v}{\partial x} \right) \right.$$
$$+ \left. \left. \alpha_{22}\left(v\,\frac{\partial u}{\partial y} - u\,\frac{\partial v}{\partial y} \right) + \alpha_2 uv \right] dx \right\},$$

and state:

GREEN'S THEOREM. *If for every standard curve C lying wholly within the region Σ the equations*

$$(9) \quad \Lambda[C, u_s] = \int\int_\sigma (f - \alpha u)dxdy,$$

$$(11) \quad \Gamma[C, v_s] = \int\int_\sigma (g - \beta v)dxdy$$

are satisfied, then the equation

$$(14) \qquad H[C, u_s, v_s] = \int \int_\sigma (vf - ug)dxdy$$

*will also be satisfied.**

This theorem contains as a special case the usual Green's theorem for the differential expression (9'). If equation (9) is to be investigated, the function $g(xy)$ in (11) may be regarded as arbitrary, and will be chosen so as best to make the equation (9) integrable, in order that a convenient function $v(xy)$ may then be utilized in connection with (9) and (14).† If $g(xy)$ is taken identically null, the function $v(xy)$ is an *integrating multiplier* for the equation (9).

50. Proof of Green's Theorem. In order to prove this theorem we follow a method worked out by C. A. Epperson,‡ the integro-differential expressions being now however somewhat simplified in comparison with his, and establish first a lemma. For this purpose the curves C are restricted to small squares about arbitrary points P as center, which are made to approach P as a limit; for convenience, the values of a function at P and at a point on C are designated by subscripts P and s respectively. The lemma follows:

LEMMA. *With the above restrictions upon the curves C, the relations*

$$(15) \qquad (f - \alpha u)_P = \lim_{\sigma=P} \frac{1}{\sigma} \Lambda[C, u_s],$$

$$(16) \qquad (g - \beta v)_P = \lim_{\sigma=P} \frac{1}{\sigma} \Gamma[C, v_s]$$

* Special cases of this form of Green's theorem were proved independently by C. W. Oseen, *Rendiconti del Circolo Matematico di Palermo*, vol. 38 (1914), pp. 167–179; and G. C. Evans, *Transactions of the American Mathematical Society*, vol. 15 (1914), pp. 477–496. A similar theorem has been proved for hydrodynamics by C. W. Oseen (see the footnote to the title of Lecture IV).

The theorem also holds if the curves C are restricted to rectangles or even to circles (see the second method of proof).

† Such for instance as the *Parametrix*, defined by Hilbert.

‡ Epperson, *Bulletin of the American Mathematical Society*, vol. 22 (1915), pp. 17–26.

holding for every point P within Σ, imply the relation

$$(17) \qquad (vf - ug)_P = \lim_{\sigma=P} \frac{1}{\sigma} H[C, u_s, v_s].$$

Form the function

$$(vf - ug)_P = \lim_{\sigma=P} \frac{1}{\sigma} \left\{ v_P \Lambda[C, u_s] - u_P \Gamma[C, v_s] \right.$$
$$\left. - \left(\left(\frac{\partial \alpha_1}{\partial x} + \frac{\partial \alpha_2}{\partial y} \right) uv \right)_P \right\}$$

from (15) and (16), with the aid of (12). If we write now the difference of the expression just given and that given by (17), we note that it consists of the quantities:

$$(i) \qquad -\left[\left(\frac{\partial \alpha_1}{\partial x} + \frac{\partial \alpha_2}{\partial y} \right) uv \right]_P ,$$

$$(ii) \qquad \frac{1}{\sigma} \int \left\{ \alpha_{11} \left[(v_P - v_s) \frac{\partial u_s}{\partial x} - (u_P - u_s) \frac{\partial v_s}{\partial x} \right] \right.$$
$$+ \alpha_{12}(v_P - v_s) \frac{\partial u_s}{\partial y} - \alpha_{21}(u_P - u_s) \frac{\partial v_s}{\partial y}$$
$$\left. + \alpha_1[(v_P - v_s)u_s + u_P v_s] \right\} dy,$$

and a similar integral (iii), taken with regard to the variable x.

In the expression (ii), we have by the law of the mean:

$$v_P - v_s = \frac{\partial v_{P'}}{\partial x}(x_P - x_s) + \frac{\partial v_{P'}}{\partial y}(y_P - y_s),$$

where P' is some point on the line connecting P and s. Since these derivatives are uniformly continuous throughout the square σ, we may write

$$\left| (v_P - v_s) - \left\{ \frac{\partial v_s}{\partial x}(x_P - x_s) + \frac{\partial v_s}{\partial y}(y_P - y_s) \right\} \right| < 2\epsilon\delta,$$

where δ is the length of one side of σ, and ϵ may be made small with δ, uniformly for all points in σ. On account of the uniformity of this condition, since we are interested only in the limit of expression (ii), the $2\epsilon\delta$ contributes nothing to the value of $1/\sigma$ times the integral, and we may replace everywhere in (ii) the quantity $(v_P - v_s)$ by the quantity

$$\frac{\partial v_s}{\partial x}(x_P - x_s) + \frac{\partial v_s}{\partial y}(y_P - y_s),$$

with a similar substitution for the quantity $(u_P - u_s)$.

If now we denote the two opposite vertices of the square by $(x_1 y_1)$ and $(x_2 y_2)$ the expression (ii) becomes the difference of two integrals of the same expression, one along $x = x_1$, the other along $x = x_2$, and we have for it the value

$$\frac{1}{\sigma}\int_{y_1}^{y_2}\Big\{\Big[\alpha_{11}\Big(\frac{\partial v}{\partial y}\frac{\partial u}{\partial x} - \frac{\partial u}{\partial y}\frac{\partial v}{\partial x}\Big)\Big]_{x_1}^{x_2}(y_P - y)$$
$$+ \Big[\Big(\alpha_{12}\frac{\partial v}{\partial x}\frac{\partial u}{\partial y} - \alpha_{21}\frac{\partial u}{\partial x}\frac{\partial v}{\partial y}\Big)(x_P - x)\Big]_{x_1}^{x_2}$$
$$+ \Big[(\alpha_{12} - \alpha_{21})\frac{\partial v}{\partial y}\frac{\partial u}{\partial y}\Big]_{x_1}^{x_2}(y_P - y) + \Big[\alpha_1\frac{\partial v}{\partial x}u(x_P - x)\Big]_{x_1}^{x_2}$$
$$+ \Big[\alpha_1\frac{\partial v}{\partial y}u\Big]_{x_1}^{x_2}(y_P - y) + \Big[\alpha v\Big]_{x_1}^{x_2}u_P\Big\}\,dy,$$

where the quantities x_2 and x_1, above and below the bracket, indicate that the value of the expression within, when the arguments are $(x_1 y)$, is to be subtracted from its value when the arguments are $(x_2 y)$.

If we apply the law of the mean to the above integral, we notice that the terms which are multiplied into $y_P - y$ will disappear in the limit as we divide by σ and let σ approach zero, since, on account of the uniform continuity of the quantities involved, the integration will in each case yield an infinitesimal of higher order than σ. If in addition we make use of our special hypothesis that $x_P - x_1$ is equal to $x_2 - x_P$ we obtain for the limit of the whole expression (ii) the quantity

(18)
$$-\Big(\alpha_{12}\frac{\partial v}{\partial x}\frac{\partial u}{\partial y} - \alpha_{21}\frac{\partial u}{\partial x}\frac{\partial v}{\partial y}\Big)_P$$
$$-\Big(\alpha_1\frac{\partial v}{\partial x}u\Big)_P + \Big(\frac{\partial(\alpha_1 v)}{\partial x}u\Big)_P,$$

which is

$$(18') \qquad -\left(\alpha_{12} \frac{\partial v}{\partial x} \frac{\partial u}{\partial y} - \alpha_{21} \frac{\partial u}{\partial x} \frac{\partial v}{\partial y} \right)_P - \left(uv \frac{\partial \alpha_1}{\partial x} \right)_P.$$

In a precisely similar manner we find for the limit of the expression (*iii*) the quantity

$$-\left(\alpha_{21} \frac{\partial v}{\partial y} \frac{\partial u}{\partial x} - \alpha_{12} \frac{\partial u}{\partial y} \frac{\partial v}{\partial x} \right)_P + \left(uv \frac{\partial \alpha_2}{\partial y} \right)_P.$$

Hence the sum of (*i*), (*ii*) and (*iii*) has the limit zero, and the lemma is proved.

We see that all the limits involved in the proof of the lemma just given are uniform with respect to the point P. Hence we have the further lemma that *the limit specified in equation* (17) *is uniform with respect to the point* P, *for all points* P *in a region enclosed by any standard curve* C *lying wholly within* Σ, *and therefore that*

$$(19) \qquad \left| (vf - ug)_P - \frac{1}{\sigma} H[\bar{C}, u_s, v_s] \right| \leq \eta\sigma,$$

where η *is independent of* P, *and* C *is the boundary of the square* σ.

If now we return to the original theorem, the proof is immediate. For if we divide up the region σ, bounded by the curve C, by a square grating, each square being of size σ_r, and denote by S_r the outside boundary of the collection of squares entirely enclosed within σ, we shall have

$$\left| \int\int_{\sigma_r} (vf - ug)d\sigma - (vf - ug)_P \sigma_r \right| \leq \epsilon\sigma_r,$$

where P is the center of the square σ_r, and ϵ can be made uniformly as small as we please with σ_r, for all squares σ_r. Hence we have the equation

$$\left| \int\int_{S_r} (vf - ug)d\sigma - H[S_r, u_s, v_s] \right| \leq (\eta + \epsilon)\Sigma\sigma_r,$$

and, since we can make the grating as minute as we please, by further subdivision, without changing the outside boundary S_r, the equation

$$\int\int_{S_r} (vf - ug)d\sigma = H[S_r, u_s, v_s].$$

If, having found this equation, we now change S_r as we again decrease σ_r, keeping however S_r the largest possible boundary of squares enclosed in C, and take the limit of both sides as σ_r approaches zero, we have

$$\int\int_{\sigma} (vf - ug)d\sigma = H[C, u_s, v_s],$$

since the integrands in the curvilinear integrals constituting the right-hand member are uniformly continuous functions of their arguments. This completes the proof.

51. A Proof by Approximating Polynomials. An interesting method of proof of this same theorem is afforded by the method of approximating polynomials. In what follows only a special case is treated. Let u, v and their first partial derivatives, and f and g be limited and continuous within and on the boundary of a rectangular region D: $a \leq x \leq b$, $a \leq y \leq b$, and consider the theorem with special reference to Poisson's equation:

THEOREM. *If for every standard curve enclosed entirely within the region D the two equations*

$$(20) \qquad \int_c \frac{\partial u}{\partial n} ds = \int\int f(xy)dxdy,$$

$$(21) \qquad \int_c \frac{\partial v}{\partial n} ds = \int\int g(xy)dxdy$$

are satisfied, then the equation

$$(22) \qquad \int_c \left(v \frac{\partial u}{\partial n} - u \frac{\partial v}{\partial n} \right) ds = \int\int (vf - ug)dxdy$$

will also be satisfied.[*]

Denote by k_μ the quantity

$$k_\mu = 2 \frac{(2\mu)!!}{(2\mu + 1)!!},$$

and by D' the region $a' \leq x \leq b'$, $a' \leq y \leq b'$, where a' and b' are fixed so that $a < a' < b' < b$. We shall prove the theorem first for the region D'. For the sake of convenience in notation we assume that $0 < a < b < 1$.

---

[*] A different method of considering $\nabla^2 u$ as a single differential operator has been developed by H. Petrini, *Acta Matematica*, vol. 31 (1908), see p. 181. Green's theorem may also be proved for this operator.

The polynomial

$$(23) \qquad P_\mu[u] = \frac{1}{k_\mu{}^2} \int\!\!\int_D u(\theta\psi)\{1 - (\theta - x)^2\}^\mu \{1 - (\psi - y)^2\}^\mu d\theta d\psi$$

converges uniformly, as μ becomes infinite, to the function $u(xy)$ throughout the square D'; moreover its first partial derivatives are polynomials which converge uniformly to the first partial derivatives of $u(xy)$, throughout the same region.*

If the equation (20) *is satisfied the polynomial* $\nabla^2 P_\mu[u]$ *converges uniformly throughout* D' *to the function* $- f(xy)$, *as* μ *becomes infinite.*

To prove this, notice that as C approaches $(x_0 y_0)$ uniformly, we have

$$\lim_{\sigma = 0} \frac{1}{\sigma} \int\!\!\int f(\theta\psi) d\theta d\psi = f(x_0 y_0)$$

and

$$\lim_{\sigma = 0} \frac{1}{\sigma} \int_C \frac{\partial P_\mu[u]}{\partial n} ds = - \nabla^2 P_\mu[u],$$

where $(x_0 y_0)$ is any point in D'. Also:

$$P_\mu[u] = \int_{a-x}^{b-x} d\theta \int_{a-y}^{b-y} u(\theta + x, \psi + y) \frac{(1 - \theta^2)^\mu (1 - \psi^2)^\mu}{k_\mu{}^2} d\psi$$

and

$$(24) \quad \lim_{\mu = \infty} P_\mu[u] = \lim_{\mu = \infty} \int_{-\epsilon}^{\epsilon} d\theta \int_{-\epsilon}^{\epsilon} u(\theta + x, \psi + y) \frac{(1 - \theta^2)^\mu (1 - \psi^2)^\mu}{k_\mu{}^2} d\psi$$

uniformly for all points in D' provided that ϵ is taken less than both $a' - a$ and $b' - b$. It is well known moreover that

$$(25) \quad \lim_{\mu = \infty} \frac{\partial}{\partial x} P_\mu[u]$$
$$= \lim_{\mu = \infty} \int_{-\epsilon}^{\epsilon} d\theta \int_{-\epsilon}^{\epsilon} \frac{\partial u(\theta + x, \psi + y)}{\partial x} \frac{(1 - \theta^2)^\mu (1 - \psi^2)^\mu}{k_\mu{}^2} d\psi,$$

and similarly for $\partial P_\mu[u]/\partial y$.

If the integral in the right-hand member of (24) is denoted by $\overline{P}_\mu[u]$ the integral in the right-hand member of (25) will be $\partial \overline{P}_\mu[u]/\partial x$. Further, the quantity

$$Q_\mu[u] = P_\mu[u] - \overline{P}_\mu[u]$$

will be a function of x, y which, on account of the hypothesis made in regard to ϵ, will have continuous limited derivatives of the first and second orders, which as we see by calculation, all uniformly approach zero, as μ becomes infinite. Hence from (25) follows the equation

$$(26) \qquad \nabla^2 P_\mu[u] = - \lim_{\sigma = 0} \frac{1}{\sigma} \int_C \frac{\partial \overline{P}_\mu[u]}{\partial n} ds + \nabla^2 Q_\mu[u],$$

where $\nabla^2 Q_\mu[u]$ approaches zero uniformly as μ becomes infinite.

* De la Vallée-Poussin, Cours d'analyse infinitésimale, Louvain (1912), vol. 2, p. 131. The idea of this proof is suggested by the very short proof of the theorem of vol. 2, p. 24.

But we have

$$\int_C \frac{\partial \overline{P}_\mu}{\partial n} ds = \int_{-\epsilon}^\epsilon d\theta \int_{-\epsilon}^\epsilon d\psi \frac{(1 - \theta^2)^\mu (1 - \psi^2)^\mu}{k_\mu^2} \int_{C,} \frac{\partial u(\theta + x, \psi + y)}{\partial n} ds,$$

in which the differentiation and the inner integration are carried out on the variables x, y. Hence, by (20), we have

$$\frac{1}{\sigma} \int_C \frac{\partial \overline{P}_\mu}{\partial n} ds = \int_{-\epsilon}^\epsilon d\theta \int_{-\epsilon}^\epsilon d\psi \frac{(1 - \theta^2)^\mu (1 - \psi^2)^\mu}{k_\mu^2} \frac{1}{\sigma} \int\int f(\theta + x, \psi + y) dx dy.$$

Here, however, since f is continuous in both arguments, the quantity

$$\frac{1}{\sigma} \int\int f(\theta + x, \psi + y) dx dy$$

differs from $f(\theta + x_0, \psi + y_0)$ by an amount which is numerically less than a certain infinitesimal η, which approaches zero uniformly with σ for all values of θ and ψ in the range $\{-\epsilon, \epsilon\}$. Therefore, finally, we have

$$(27) \quad \lim_{\sigma = 0} \frac{1}{\sigma} \int_C \frac{\partial \overline{P}_\mu}{\partial n} ds = \int_{-\epsilon}^\epsilon d\theta \int_{-\epsilon}^\epsilon f(\theta + x_0, \psi + y_0) \frac{(1 - \theta^2)^\mu (1 - \psi^2)^\mu}{k_\mu^2} d\psi.$$

By combining now (27) and (26), it follows that

$$- \lim_{\mu = \infty} \nabla^2 P_\mu[u] = \lim_{\mu = \infty} \int_{-\epsilon}^\epsilon d\theta \int_{-\epsilon}^\epsilon f(\theta + x_0, \psi + y_0) \frac{(1 - \theta^2)^\mu (1 - \psi^2)^\mu}{k_\mu^2} d\psi$$

uniformly for all values of $x_0 y_0$ in D'. But this last limit is precisely $f(x_0 y_0)$, so that the lemma is proved.

It is now easy to complete the main theorem. In fact, since $P_\mu[u]$ and $P_\mu[v]$ are polynomials, Green's theorem applies directly to them, as usually stated; viz.,

$$\int_C \left\{ P_\mu[v] \frac{\partial P_\mu[u]}{\partial n} - P_\mu[u] \frac{\partial P_\mu[v]}{\partial n} \right\} ds$$
$$= - \int\int_\sigma \{P_\mu[v] \nabla^2 P_\mu[u] - P_\mu[u] \nabla^2 P_\mu[v]\} d\sigma.$$

Since, however, by (20) and (21), $P_\mu[u]$, $P_\mu[v]$, $\nabla^2 P_\mu[u]$, $\nabla^2 P_\mu[v]$ converge uniformly throughout D' to the functions u, v, f, g respectively, the limits of the integrals in the last equation will be the integrals of the limits; and for any curve C in D' the result will follow:

$$\int_C \left\{ v \frac{\partial u}{\partial n} - u \frac{\partial v}{\partial n} \right\} ds = \int\int \{vf - ug\} dx dy.$$

But this result holds also for any standard curve lying wholly inside of D; for a region D' may be drawn so as to contain this curve, since it has a nearest point to each boundary of D.

52. Change of Variable. With regard to the equations (9) and (11) let us make a transformation

$$(28) \qquad \xi = \varphi(xy), \qquad \eta = \theta(xy),$$

where φ and θ are two functions continuous with their first derivatives in the given (simply connected) region, and let the Jacobian, $J = d(\xi\eta)/d(xy)$, not vanish in this region.

If we consider $\Lambda[C, u_s]$ and $\iint (f - \alpha u)dxdy$ as functionals of C, and u, α, $\cdots$ as functions of (x, y), leaving them unchanged in value as they are moved to the corresponding curves and points of the transformed plane, the integro-differential equation (9) is transformed into a similar equation, with $\bar{u} = u$, and

$$J\bar{\alpha}_{11} = \alpha_{11}\left(\frac{\partial\varphi}{\partial x}\right)^2 + (\alpha_{12} + \alpha_{21})\frac{\partial\varphi}{\partial x}\frac{\partial\varphi}{\partial y} + \alpha_{22}\left(\frac{\partial\varphi}{\partial y}\right)^2,$$

$$J\bar{\alpha}_{12} = \alpha_{11}\frac{\partial\varphi}{\partial x}\frac{\partial\theta}{\partial x} + \alpha_{12}\frac{\partial\varphi}{\partial x}\frac{\partial\theta}{\partial y} + \alpha_{21}\frac{\partial\varphi}{\partial y}\frac{\partial\theta}{\partial x} + \alpha_{22}\frac{\partial\varphi}{\partial y}\frac{\partial\theta}{\partial y},$$

$$(29) \quad J\bar{\alpha}_{21} = \alpha_{11}\frac{\partial\varphi}{\partial x}\frac{\partial\theta}{\partial x} + \alpha_{12}\frac{\partial\varphi}{\partial y}\frac{\partial\theta}{\partial x} + \alpha_{21}\frac{\partial\varphi}{\partial x}\frac{\partial\theta}{\partial y} + \alpha_{22}\frac{\partial\varphi}{\partial y}\frac{\partial\theta}{\partial y},$$

$$J\bar{\alpha}_{22} = \alpha_{11}\left(\frac{\partial\theta}{\partial x}\right)^2 + (\alpha_{12} + \alpha_{21})\frac{\partial\theta}{\partial x}\frac{\partial\theta}{\partial y} + \alpha_{22}\left(\frac{\partial\theta}{\partial y}\right)^2,$$

$$J\bar{\alpha}_1 = \alpha_1\frac{\partial\varphi}{\partial x} + \alpha_2\frac{\partial\varphi}{\partial y}, \qquad J\alpha_2 = \alpha_1\frac{\partial\theta}{\partial x} + \alpha_2\frac{\partial\theta}{\partial y},$$

$$J\bar{\alpha} = \alpha, \qquad\qquad J\bar{f} = f.$$

The expression

$$(30) \qquad\qquad I = (\alpha_{12} + \alpha_{21})^2 - 4\alpha_{11}\alpha_{22}$$

is an invariant of this transformation. In fact we have $\bar{I} = I$. The expression

$$(31) \qquad T(dx, dy) = \alpha_{11}dy^2 - (\alpha_{12} + \alpha_{21})dydx + \alpha_{22}dx^2$$

is a covariant; in fact,

$$\bar{T}(d\xi, d\eta) = JT(dx, dy).$$

This same transformation of the plane transforms the adjoint equation in a similar manner, every α and $\bar{\alpha}$ in (29) being replaced by the corresponding β or $\bar{\beta}$. Moreover the relation of adjointness is preserved by the transformation. To insure this, however, it is necessary to assume the existence of the second derivatives of the functions φ and ψ, since otherwise the coefficients in the transformation of the adjoint equation will not be defined.[*] To prove this fact, the only difficulty is connected with the last of the equations (12). This can be written in the equivalent form:

$$(32) \qquad \int\int (\beta - \alpha)dxdy = \int_C \alpha_1 dy - \alpha_2 dx,$$

which is an invariant relation, since each member is a functional of C, which is seen to be unchanged in value by the transformation, on account of the formulae (29). Hence the equation (32) will be satisfied by the transformed quantities.

We can make a transformation

$$(33) \qquad u = \psi(xy)\bar{u}$$

of the dependent variable. The function $\bar{u}$ will satisfy a new integro-differential equation of the same kind as before, with

$$\bar{\alpha}_{ij} = \psi\alpha_{ij}, \qquad \bar{\alpha} = \psi\alpha, \qquad \bar{f} = f,$$

$$(34) \qquad \bar{\alpha}_1 = \alpha_{11}\frac{\partial\psi}{\partial x} + \alpha_{12}\frac{\partial\psi}{\partial y} + \alpha_1\psi,$$

$$\bar{\alpha}_2 = \alpha_{21}\frac{\partial\psi}{\partial x} + \alpha_{22}\frac{\partial\psi}{\partial y} + \alpha_2\psi.$$

The quantity I will be an invariant, and the quantity T a covariant of this new transformation.

The relation of adjointness will be preserved if at the same time we make a transformation of the adjoint equation given by the formulæ:

$$\bar{v} = v, \qquad \bar{g} = g, \qquad \bar{\beta}_{ij} = \psi\beta_{ij},$$

$$\bar{\beta}_1 = -\beta_{11}\frac{\partial\psi}{\partial x} - \beta_{21}\frac{\partial\psi}{\partial y} + \beta_1\psi,$$

[*] It is possible, however, to use less restrictive conditions if the analysis is based on (32) instead of the last of the equations (12). This would demand a slightly different treatment of Green's theorem, breaking thereby from the theory of the Riemann integral.

$$(34') \qquad \bar{\beta}_2 = -\beta_{12}\frac{\partial\psi}{\partial x} - \beta_{22}\frac{\partial\psi}{\partial y} + \beta_2\psi,$$

$$\bar{\beta} = \beta\psi - \beta_1\frac{\partial\psi}{\partial x} - \beta_2\frac{\partial\psi}{\partial y} + \frac{\partial}{\partial x}\left(\beta_{11}\frac{\partial\psi}{\partial x} + \beta_{21}\frac{\partial\psi}{\partial y}\right)$$
$$+ \frac{\partial}{\partial y}\left(\beta_{12}\frac{\partial\psi}{\partial x} + \beta_{22}\frac{\partial\psi}{\partial y}\right).$$

The expressions I and T will also of course be respectively invariant and covariant of this transformation.

For this last transformation to be defined it is necessary that the second derivatives of ψ exist.

53. The Three Types of Equation. The directions defined by the covariant equation

$$(35) \qquad\qquad T(dx, dy) = 0$$

or, what is the same thing,

$$(35') \qquad\qquad 2\alpha_{11}dy = (\alpha_{12} + \alpha_{21} \pm \sqrt{I})dx$$

are called the *characteristic directions*, and the solutions of the equation, the *characteristic curves*. Characteristic directions go over into characteristic directions, by any of the transformations considered. There are, then, three cases to consider with respect to any point of the region; if the characteristic directions are real and distinct at a point the equation (9) is said to be *hyperbolic* at the point; if they are real and coincident the equation is *parabolic*; if they are not real, the equation is *elliptic*. Equations (9) and (11) are of the same type, and the type is unchanged by any real transformation of the kinds considered.

The three types of equations can be reduced by real transformations of the independent and dependent variables to three normal forms respectively. We assume for convenience that in the region we are investigating we have $\alpha_{11} \neq 0$, and also that the first derivatives of the coefficients α_{ij}, α_i, are continuous as well as the coefficients themselves. This last restriction is not entirely necessary, but we are more interested in reducing the restrictions on the solutions than on the coefficients.

The following equation is an identity:

$$(36) \quad \int_c \left\{ \alpha_{12} \frac{\partial u}{\partial y} dy - \alpha_{21} \frac{\partial u}{\partial x} dx \right\}$$

$$= \int_c \left\{ \left(\frac{\alpha_{12} + \alpha_{21}}{2} \frac{\partial u}{\partial y} + \frac{\partial}{\partial y} \frac{-\alpha_{12} + \alpha_{21}}{2} u \right) dy \right.$$

$$\left. - \left(\frac{\alpha_{12} + \alpha_{21}}{2} \frac{\partial u}{\partial x} + \frac{\partial}{\partial x} \frac{\alpha_{12} - \alpha_{21}}{2} u \right) dx, \right.$$

and it may be proved in the same way as the extension of Green's theorem, already given.*

The normal forms are then obtained, as in the theory of linear partial differential equations, to be the following:

Elliptic:

$$(37) \quad \int_c \left\{ \frac{\partial u}{\partial x} + \alpha_1 u \right\} dy - \left\{ \frac{\partial u}{\partial y} + \alpha_2 u \right\} dx = \int\int (f - \alpha u) dx dy.$$

Hyperbolic:

$$(37') \quad \int_c \left\{ \frac{\partial u}{\partial y} + \alpha_1 u \right\} dy - \left\{ \frac{\partial u}{\partial x} + \alpha_2 u \right\} dx = \int\int (f - \alpha u) dx dy.$$

Parabolic:

$$(37'') \quad \int_c \alpha_1 u \, dy - \left\{ \frac{\partial u}{\partial y} + \alpha_2 u \right\} dx = \int\int (f - \alpha u) dx dy.$$

With the hypotheses just made, the new functions α_1, α_2 are continuous, but do not necessarily have continuous first partial derivatives. If we desire this last property, we must assume that the original coefficients α_{ij} possess continuous *second* partial derivatives. This assumption is necessary if we desire to use Green's theorem; without its use, however, we can still establish the existence, though perhaps not the uniqueness, of solutions of the equations, with reference to the usual boundary value problems.

The different types of equations do not arise in practise, however, by transformations of more general forms, determined by

---

* The most direct proof is that by approximating polynomials.

the values of I, as in the preceding paragraphs, but appear separately in conformity to certain types of physical problems, such as, for instance, those of potential, flow of heat, and vibration. Hence the transformations and the assumptions on which they are based are not so likely to present themselves in applications to physics. Here we have not space to give the detailed treatment of these three types, and therefore confine ourselves to the one which is perhaps least extensively studied, imposing merely the few conditions on the coefficients which are sufficient for the desired analysis of this type.

§ 3. The Parabolic Integro-Differential Equation of Bôcher Type

54. Derivation of the Equation for the Flow of Heat. Consider, for simplicity, a bar of length l, insulated except at the ends, and in particular the portion of it between $y = y_1$ and $y = y_2$ at times $x = x_1$ and $x = x_2$. The amount of heat that is contained in this portion of the bar at time x_2 is $\int_{y_1}^{y_2} cu(x_2, y)dy$, and the amount at time x_1 is $\int_{y_1}^{y_2} cu(x_1y)dy$, where c is the specific heat, and u the temperature. On the other hand, by Newton's law, the amount that flows out through the end y_2 is $\int_{x_1}^{x_2} k\partial u(x, y_2)/\partial y dx$ and the amount that flows in through the end y_1 is $\int_{x_1}^{x_2} k\partial u(xy_1)/\partial y dx$, k being the conductivity. Since the difference of the first two quantities must be equal to the difference of the second, *we have for any rectangle in the x, y plane*:

$$(38) \qquad \int cudy + k\frac{\partial u}{\partial y}dx = 0,$$

if there are no interior sources of heat.

If there are interior sources of heat which contribute an amount $\int_{y_1}^{y_2} dy \int_{x_1}^{x_2} f(xy)dx$ to the quantity of heat contained in the portion y_1y_2 of the bar, the equation becomes*

$$(39) \qquad \int cudy + k\frac{\partial u}{\partial y}dx = \int\int f(xy)dxdy.$$

If c and k are constants they can be absorbed by a change of variable, so that we shall have

$$(38') \qquad \int udy + \frac{\partial u}{\partial y}dx = 0,$$

$$(39') \qquad \int udy + \frac{\partial u}{\partial y}dx = \int\int f(xy)dxdy.$$

In three dimensions, corresponding to (38') we have the equation

$$(40) \qquad \underset{t=t_2}{\int\int\int} udxdydz - \underset{t=t_1}{\int\int\int} udxdydz = \int_{t_1}^{t_2}dt\int\int\frac{\partial u}{\partial n}d\sigma,$$

which may be rewritten as an integral over a three-dimensional hyperspace, immersed in a 4-space.

55. The Dirichlet Problem. Instead of (39'), we consider the more general equation

$$(41) \qquad \int_C udy - \left(-\frac{\partial u}{\partial y} + \alpha_2 u\right)dx = \int\int_\sigma (f - \alpha u)dxdy,$$

where C is any closed standard curve within the given region, and the functions f, α, α_2, $\partial\alpha_2/\partial y$ are continuous within and on the boundary of the given region.

The adjoint equation to (41) is

$$(41') \qquad \int_C - vdy - \left(-\frac{\partial v}{\partial y} + \beta_2 v\right)dx = \int\int_\sigma (g - \beta v)dxdy$$

in which

$$\beta_2 = -\alpha_2 \qquad \text{and} \qquad \beta = \alpha + \frac{\partial\alpha_2}{\partial y}.$$

---

* It would be more natural to represent the right-hand member of this equation by a two-dimensional Stieltjes integral (an additive and perhaps absolutely continuous functional of the rectangle C). We restrict ourselves to the case where f itself exists, and is continuous. This same note applies of course to (5).

If g is a continuous function the coefficients of (41′) satisfy the same conditions as the corresponding coefficients of (41).

We consider a region also slightly more general than in the corresponding physical problem. Denote by $_{x_0}R_{x_1}$ (following a notation used by W. A. Hurwitz) a

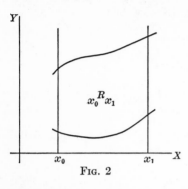

Y

$_{x_0}{}^R{}_{x_1}$

x_0 x_1 X

FIG. 2

region bounded on the left by the line $x = x_0$, on the right by the line $x = x_1$, above by the curve $y = \xi_2(x)$, and below by the curve $y = \xi_1(x)$. The functions ξ_1 and ξ_2 are to be continuous with their first derivatives, and are to have only a finite number of maxima and minima in the interval under consideration. Moreover, $\xi_1(x) > \xi_2(x)$, for $x \geqq x_0$.

We shall investigate solutions of (41) which are continuous with a continuous derivative in regard to y within and on the boundary of $_{x_0}R_{x_1}$ (called *regular solutions*), and take on a continuous chain of boundary values along the open contour $_{x_0}{}^t{}_{x_1}$, comprised by the parts $x = x_0$, $y = \xi_2(x)$ and $y = \xi_1(x)$ of the boundary of $_{x_0}R_{x_1}$. *There is one and only one such solution.*

Analogously, there is one and only one regular solution of the adjoint equation (41′) in the region $_{x_0}R_{x_1}$ which takes on given values along the contour comprised by $x = x_1$, $y = \xi_1(x)$ and $y = \xi_2(x)$. The proofs of the two existence theorems are similar, and it is therefore necessary to deal only with one.

56. The Uniqueness of the Solution. Define the function

$$(42) \qquad h_{\alpha\beta}(xy \,|\, x'y') = \frac{(y' - y)^{\alpha}}{(x' - x)^{\beta}} e^{-\frac{(y'-y)^2}{4(x'-x)}}.$$

The function $h_{0\frac{1}{2}}$ as a function of x, y is a solution of the adjoint of (38′), since it is seen by differentiation to be a solution of the equation

$$\frac{\partial^2 v}{\partial y^2} + \frac{\partial v}{\partial x} = 0.$$

As a function of x', y' it is a solution of (38') itself. Its derivative in regard to y' is

$$\frac{\partial h_{0\frac{1}{2}}}{\partial y'} = - \tfrac{1}{2} h_{1, \frac{3}{2}},$$

and both $h_{0\frac{1}{2}}$ and $h_{1\frac{3}{2}}$ are integrable over the region $_{x_0}R_{x'}$. Moreover,

$$(43) \qquad \lim_{\bar{x}=x'-0} \frac{1}{2\sqrt{\pi}} \int_a^b \varphi(y) h_{0\frac{1}{2}}(\bar{x}y \,|\, x'y') dy = \varphi(y')$$

if $\xi_1(x') < y' < \xi_2(x')$, y' being between a and b, and $\varphi(y)$ is integrable, and continuous at $y = y'$.*

If we now define the Green's function $g(xy \,|\, x'y')$ for (41) by the formula

$$(44) \qquad g(xy \,|\, x'y') = h_{0\frac{1}{2}}(xy \,|\, x'y') + g'(xy \,|\, x'y'),$$

where for a point $(x'y')$ inside $_{x_0}R_{x_1}$, $g(xy \,|\, x'y')$ is in x, y a solution of the adjoint equation (41'), and $g'(xy \,|\, x'y')$ is a regular function which vanishes on the line $x = x'$ and on $y = \xi_1(x)$ and $y = \xi_2(x)$ takes on the negatives of the values of $h_{0\frac{1}{2}}$, then we have by a direct application of Green's theorem:

$$(45) \qquad \begin{aligned} 2\sqrt{\pi} u(x'y') = - &\int_{x_0^r x'} \left\{ u(xy) g(xy \,|\, x'y') dy \right. \\ &\left. - u(xy) \frac{\partial g(xy \,|\, x'y')}{\partial y} dx \right\} + \int\int f(xy) g(xy \,|\, x'y') dx dy, \end{aligned}$$

the term involving α_2 dropping out, since $dx = 0$ when $g \neq 0$, on the boundary.

On account of the explicit formula (45), the solution must be unique, if regular solutions of (41) and (41') taking on assigned boundary values exist.

57. Existence of Solutions. On account of the uniqueness of solutions of (41), there will be one and only one solution in the case when

$$\alpha_2 \equiv f \equiv \alpha \equiv 0,$$

---

* For a proof of these theorems see E. Levi, *Annali di Matematica*, vol. 14 (1908), p. 187, or W. A. Hurwitz, Randwertaufgaben der linearen partiellen Differentialgleichungen, Dissertation, Gottingen (1911).

namely, the known solution of the equation

(46) $$\frac{\partial^2 u}{\partial y^2} - \frac{\partial u}{\partial x} = 0.$$

In particular, (46) will have a Green's function $G(xy\,|\,x'y')$.
The function

$$u(x'y') = \bar{u}(x'y') + \frac{1}{2\sqrt{\pi}} \iint\limits_{x_0 R_{x'}} G(xy\,|\,x'y')f(xy)dxdy,$$

where $\bar{u}(x'y')$ is the solution of (46) which takes on the given
boundary values on $_{x_0}r_{x_1}$, will be the unique regular solution of

$$\int_C u\,dy - \left(-\frac{\partial u}{\partial y} \right)dx = \iint f dxdy,$$

which takes on the same boundary values. In fact, we may
differentiate under the integral sign to find $\partial u/\partial x'$, and by
substituting directly into the equation, and changing the order
of integration, verify that the equation is satisfied. As is well
known, the integral in the second member vanishes when (x', y')
is a point of the contour $_{x_0}r_{x_1}$.

Hence the unique regular solution of (41) must satisfy the
equation:

(47) $$u(x'y') = \bar{u}(x'y') + \frac{1}{2\sqrt{\pi}} \iint\limits_{x_0 R_{x'}} G(xy\,|\,x'y') \left\{ f - \alpha u \right.$$
$$\left. - \frac{\partial}{\partial y}(\alpha_2 u) \right\}_{xy} dxdy,$$

since, with our assumptions, we have

$$\int_C \alpha_2 u\,dy = - \iint \frac{\partial}{\partial y}(\alpha_2 u)dxdy.$$

Hence, finally, if we write

$$\partial_{x'y'}u = - \alpha(x'y')u(x'y') - \frac{\partial}{\partial y'}[\alpha_2(x'y')u(x'y')],$$

$$\varphi(x'y') = \bar{u}(x'y') + \frac{1}{2\sqrt{\pi}} \iint G(xy\,|\,x'y')f(xy)dxdy,$$

the quantity $\partial_{x'y'}u$ must satisfy the integral equation

$$\partial_{x'y'}u(x'y') = \partial_{x'y'}\varphi(x'y')$$

(48)
$$+ \frac{1}{2\sqrt{\pi}} \int\int_{x_0 R_{x'}} \partial_{x'y'}G(xy|x'y')\partial_{xy}u(xy)dxdy.$$

In this integral equation, the first term of the right-hand member is a continuous function.

On the other hand we know that there is a unique continuous solution of (48), which yields when applied to (47), since we can differentiate once with respect to y under the integral sign, a regular solution of that equation, and therefore a regular solution of (41).

We can as a matter of fact go still further than this. There is a unique solution $k(xy|x'y')$ of the equations

$$k(xy|x'y') + \frac{1}{2\sqrt{\pi}}\partial_{x'y'}G(xy|x'y')$$

(49)
$$= \frac{1}{2\sqrt{\pi}} \int\int_{x R_{x'}} k(xy|\xi\eta)\partial_{x'y'}G(\xi\eta|x'y')d\xi d\eta$$

$$= \frac{1}{2\sqrt{\pi}} \int\int_{x R_{x'}} \partial_{\xi\eta}G(xy|\xi\eta)k(\xi\eta|x'y')d\xi d\eta,$$

which is called the resolvent kernel to $\partial_{x'y'}G(xy|x'y')/2\sqrt{\pi}$, and denoted by the symbol

$$\overline{\frac{1}{2\sqrt{\pi}}\partial_{x'y'}G(xy|x'y')}.$$

The solution of (48) may then be written in the form

$$\partial_{x'y'}u(x'y') = \partial_{x'y'}\varphi(x'y')$$
$$- \int\int_{x_0 R_{x'}} \left(\overline{\frac{1}{2\sqrt{\pi}}\partial_{x'y'}G(xy|x'y')}\right)\partial_{xy}\varphi(xy)dxdy.$$

The examination of the existence and continuity of $k(xy|x'y')$ demands consideration of the uniform convergence of the same improper integrals as in the case of (48).

58. The Green's Function.   The Green's function for (41) is closely related to the function $k(xy\,|\,x'y')$. As a function of $(x'y')$ it is a solution of (41) itself, with $f \equiv 0$, and it may be deduced from this fact, and from (47), that the Green's function satisfies the equation

$$g(xy\,|\,x'y') = G(xy\,|\,x'y') + \frac{1}{2\sqrt{\pi}} \iint\limits_{xR_{x'}} G(\xi\eta\,|\,x'y')\partial_{\xi\eta}g(xy\,|\,\xi\eta)d\xi d\eta,$$

and hence the integral equation

$$\partial_{x'y'}g(xy\,|\,x'y') = \partial_{x'y'}G(xy\,|\,x'y')$$

$$+ \frac{1}{2\sqrt{\pi}} \iint\limits_{xR_{x'}} \partial_{x'y'}G(\xi\eta\,|\,x'y')\partial_{\xi\eta}g(xy\,|\,\xi\eta)d\xi d\eta.$$

Hence we have

$$(50) \qquad \partial_{x'y'}g(xy\,|\,x'y') = - 2\sqrt{\pi}\,\overline{\left(\frac{1}{2\sqrt{\pi}}\partial_{x'y'}G(xy\,|\,x'y')\right)},$$

and

$$g(xy\,|\,x'y') = G(xy\,|\,x'y')$$

$$(51)$$

$$- \iint\limits_{xR_{x'}} G(\xi\eta\,|\,x'y')\overline{\left(\frac{1}{2\sqrt{\pi}}\partial_{\xi\eta}G(xy\,|\,\xi\eta)\right)}d\xi d\eta.$$

§ 4. The Parabolic Integro-Differential Equation of the Usual Type

59. The Generalized Green's Function.   For simplicity, let us add to the conditions on the boundary of the region, the requirements $\xi_2'(x) > 0$, $\xi_1'(x) < 0$, and deal with the equation

$$\frac{\partial u}{\partial x} - \frac{\partial^2 u}{\partial y^2} = \int_{x_y}^{x} A(x,\,\xi,\,y)u(\xi,\,y)d\xi,$$

or for still greater simplicity, with its generalization:

$$(52) \qquad \int u\,dy - \left(-\frac{\partial u}{\partial y}\right)dx = \iint d\sigma \int_{x_y}^{x} A(x\xi y)u(xy)dx.$$

In these equations $(x_y,\,y)$ denotes the point on the boundary $x_0 r_x$ of which one co-ordinate is y.

If $u(xy)$ and $v(xy)$ are any two continuous functions, it may be proved by means of a change in the order of integration that the following identity holds:

$$(53) \quad \iint_{x_0 R_{x_1}} \left\{ v(xy) \int_{x_y}^{x} A(x\xi y)u(\xi y)d\xi - u(xy) \int_{x}^{x_1} A(\xi xy)v(\xi y)d\xi \right\} dxdy = 0.$$

If we define the generalized Green's function for (52) as the solution $S(xy \mid x'y')$ of the adjoint equation

$$\int - vdy - \left(-\frac{\partial v}{\partial y} \right) dx = \iint dxdy \int_{x_y}^{y} A(\xi xy)v(\xi y)d\xi,$$

which is equal to $h_{0\frac{1}{2}}$ plus a regular function which vanishes for $x = x'$, and takes on the values $- h_{0\frac{1}{2}}$ on the upper and lower boundaries, we can find a formula for it in the same way as in the case of (41). In this case, however, the fact that the quantity

$$(54) \quad u(x'y') = \frac{1}{2\sqrt{\pi}} \int_{x_0 r_{x'}} u(xy) \left\{ S(xy \mid x'y')dy - \frac{\partial}{\partial y} S(xy \mid x'y')dx \right\}$$

represents the solution of (52), which takes on the assigned boundary values depends essentially upon the identity (53). In other words, instead of Lagrange's identity we have as the basis of our extended Green's theorem an identity involving an iteration of integrals.

The case is again different from that of the integro-differential equations of so-called static type which will be treated in Lecture V, by a symbolic method, depending upon distributive and associative properties of the integral combinations involved. On the other hand, the function S for the present case may be expressed in closed form, in terms of the Green's function for the parabolic differential equation

$$\frac{\partial^2 u}{\partial y^2} = \frac{\partial u}{\partial x}.$$

§ 5. The Differential Equation of Hyperbolic Type

60. Functions of Zero Variation in Two Dimensions. A treatment of the hyperbolic equation, analogous to that just given for the parabolic equation, may be developed. Since, however, the Riemann characteristic function for the hyperbolic equation is itself regular, the treatment does not depend upon the analysis of the properties of a discontinuous principal solution, and there is not the same interest in avoiding differentiation. The resulting integral equations are however interesting; they involve both simple and double integrals.*

The equation

$$(55) \quad \begin{aligned} u(x+t+t', y+t-t') - u(x+t, y+t) \\ - u(x+t', y-t') + u(x, y) = 0, \end{aligned}$$

where t and t' are arbitrary quantities, may be replaced by the equation

$$(56) \quad \frac{\partial^2 u}{\partial x^2} - \frac{\partial^2 u}{\partial y^2} = 0$$

* The equations satisfy the conditions specified in V. Volterra, *Rendiconti della R. Accademia dei Lincei*, vol. 5 (1896), 1° sem., p. 289.

if sufficient derivatives of the function u exist. Otherwise, it is of interest to study the equation (55) directly. It may be stated geometrically in terms of an arbitrary rectangle with sides parallel to the lines $x \pm y = 0$; *the sum of the values of u at the extremities of one diagonal is equal to the sum at the extremities of the other.*

The equation (55) has been used to plot solutions of the wave equation.[*] That it holds is a necessary and sufficient condition that $u(xy)$ be a function of zero variation in two dimensions;[†] such functions are obviously not restricted to constants, as they would be in one dimension.

To solve equation (55) we define a *stair* of points. Construct a broken line, with parts parallel to the lines $x \pm y = 0$, joining two end points A and B, which do not lie on a line parallel to either of these two directions. Also, let no two parts of the broken line be collinear. The vertices of the broken line, including the end points, constitute the stair.

The *associated mesh* of a stair is the collection of intersections of all lines parallel to the directions $x \pm y = 0$, which contain a point of the stair. It may be established geometrically that *if a solution of (55) is assigned arbitrary values for the points of a stair it is determined uniquely at all the points of the associated mesh, and at no other points.*

The theorem just enunciated provides immediate proofs of existence theorems of (55), e. g., that a solution is determined uniquely by assigning arbitrary values along two lines, one parallel to $x + y = 0$ and the other parallel to $x - y = 0$; also that any solution may be written in the form

$$f(x + y) + \varphi(x - y)$$

wherever it exists. In fact, if we define two stairs as intersecting when their meshes have a point in common, we see that *we can assign arbitrary values to a solution of (55) at the points of any number of non-intersecting stairs.* If two stairs intersect, values of $u(xy)$ may be assigned on them independently, provided they are assigned so as to give the same values on the points of intersection.[‡]

[*] Professor Birkhoff calls my attention to the fact that this method is used in H. N. Davis, The Longitudinal Vibrations of a Stretched String, *Proceedings of the American Academy of Sciences*, vol. 41 (1906), pp. 693–727.

[†] De la Vallée-Poussin, *Transactions of the American Mathematical Society*, vol. 16 (1915), p. 493. A change of axes is involved.

[‡] In the same way that (56) is related to (55), Laplace's equation is related to those in which the value of a function at a point is given as the mean of its values around the vertices of a polygon of n sides of which the point is at the center. In the latter case there are properties of extension like the analytic extension of solutions of Laplace's equation. Hence in this case continuity at a point is a matter of " far-reaching " importance. See for the case of one dimension, Blumberg, *Bulletin of the American Mathematical Society*, vol. 23 (1917), p. 212; this reference considers also a generalization to two dimensions of more restricted character.

LECTURE V

DIRECT GENERALIZATIONS OF THE THEORY OF INTEGRAL
EQUATIONS*

§ 1. INTRODUCTION: SOME GENERAL PROPERTIES OF THE STIELTJES INTEGRAL

61. The Stieltjes Integral Equation. The resolution of implicit functional equations, and the form of the linear functional suggest the study of the equation

$$(1) \qquad f(x) + \int_a^b \varphi(s)d_s\alpha(xs) = 0,$$

in which the subscript s indicates that we are taking the variation in regard to s, or, more particularly,

$$(2) \qquad \varphi(x) = f(x) + \lambda \int_a^b \varphi(s)d_s\alpha(xs),$$

which is a special case of that treated in Art. 35, and yet contains many forms of mixed linear equations as special cases of itself.

* This lecture is based on the following references:

E. H. Moore, On the foundations of a theory of linear integral equations, *Bulletin of the American Mathematical Society*, vol. 18 (1912), p. 335.

V. Volterra, Papers on integro-differential equations and permutable functions, *Rendiconti della R. Accademia dei Lincei*, ser. 5, vol. 18–20 (1909–11); *Lectures delivered at the celebration of the 20th anniversary of the foundation of Clark University* (1911); Teoria delle potenze dei logaritmi e delle funzioni di composizione, *R. Accademia dei Lincei, Atti*, vol. 11 (1916), pp. 167–249. The results of the earlier papers are given in the *Leçons sur les fonctions de lignes*, Paris (1913) and in the *Vanuxem Lectures*, Princeton (1912).

G. C. Evans, Sopra L'algebra delle funzioni permutabili, *R. Accademia dei Lincei, Atti*, vol. 8 (1911); L'algebra delle funzioni permutabili e non permutabili, *Rendiconti del Circolo Matematico di Palermo*, vol. 34 (1912); The Cauchy problem for integro-differential equations, *Transactions of the American Mathematical Society*, vol. 15 (1914), pp. 215–226.

For the resolution of (2), we must first define the class L of functions $\varphi(x)$.

Represent by $t_s(xs)$ the total variation function for $\alpha(xs)$, the variable x being considered as a parameter. If for a set E of values of x, or an interval $x_1 x_2$ of values of x, the quantity $t_s(xs)$, which is of course $\leq t_s(xb)$, remains finite, $\leq T_a$, the function $\alpha(xs)$ is said to be of *uniformly limited variation* in s over the set E, or the interval $x_1 x_2$, of values of x. In this case the approximation sum approaches its limit uniformly, and the measure of the approach of the sum to the integral is given by the quantity $\omega_\delta T_a$, as follows from (16), Lecture III.

We may obtain also directly the inequality

$$(3) \qquad \left| \int_a^b \varphi(s) d_s \alpha(xs) \right| \leq M T_a,$$

where $|\varphi(x)| \leq M$.

Upon these inequalities is based the following theorem, about the continuity of Stieltjes integrals:

THEOREM. *If in the integral*

$$(4) \quad \psi(x) = \int_a^b \varphi(s) d_s \alpha(xs), \qquad \varphi(s) \text{ continuous}, \ a \leq s \leq b,$$

$\alpha(xs)$ *is of uniformly limited variation in s for x in the neighborhood of x_0, and if there is a set of values F_{x_0} of s which includes a and b and is dense in ab, such that $\alpha(xs)$ is continuous in x at x_0, for s in F_{x_0}, then $\psi(x)$ is continuous at x_0.*[*]

It is evidently then desirable, for (2), to take as the class L the class of all functions $\varphi(s)$, continuous $a \leq s \leq b$, in order to satisfy (i); the condition (ii) will also be satisfied if we take $|\lambda| < 1/T_a$, as we see by (3). Accordingly, we have the theorem:

THEOREM. *If $\alpha(xs)$ is of uniformly limited variation in s for $a \leq x \leq b$, and if for every value $x = x_0$ in this interval there is a set F_{x_0} of values of s, including a and b and dense in ab, such that if s is in F_{x_0} the function $\alpha(xs)$ is continuous in x at x_0, then equation (2) has one and only one solution $\varphi(x)$, continuous $a \leq x \leq b$, provided that λ is small enough ($|\lambda| < 1/T_a$).*

---

[*] This theorem, and the theorems of Art. 62 about the Stieltjes integral, are found in H. E. Bray, *Annals of Mathematics*, vol. 19 (1918).

62. Integrability of the Stieltjes Integral. It may be verified that *if $\alpha(xs)$ is of uniformly limited variation in s, for x in the interval $x_1 \leq x \leq x_2$, and if $\gamma(x)$ is of limited variation in that interval, then the integral*

$$(5) \qquad \theta(s) = \int_{x_1}^{x_2} \alpha(xs)d\gamma(x)$$

represents a function of limited variation. In fact, we have the inequality

$$(5') \qquad T_\theta \leq T_\alpha T_\gamma.$$

In the theorem given about equation (2), the finite jumps of $\alpha(xs)$ could themselves be functions of x in position and magnitude. For closer study, *we restrict ourselves in the remainder of this article to functions $\alpha(xs)$ which are continuous in x for all values of s,*—a restriction which demands that the finite jumps of α shall have locations independent of x. We restrict ourselves also of course to continuous functions $\varphi(x)$. With these assumptions understood, the following theorem about interchanging the order of integration may be deduced:

THEOREM. *If $\alpha(xs)$ is of uniformly limited variation in s for x in x_1x_2, and if $\gamma(x)$ is of limited variation, then we have*

$$(6) \qquad \int_a^b \varphi(s)d_s \int_{x_1}^{x_2} \alpha(xs)d\gamma(x) = \int_{x_1}^{x_2} \left[\int_a^b \varphi(s)d_s\alpha(xs) \right] d\gamma(x).$$

A corollary of this theorem, obtained by taking $\gamma(x) \equiv x$, is the formula

$$(6') \qquad \int_{x_1}^{x_2} dx \int_a^b \varphi(s)d_s\alpha(xs) = \int_a^b \varphi(s)d_s \int_{x_1}^{x_2} \alpha(xs)dx.$$

Upon the formula (6) may be constructed the Volterra theory of iterated kernels, and the Volterra relation. The latter takes the form

$$(7) \qquad \begin{aligned} \alpha(xs) + A_\lambda(xs) &= \lambda \int_a^b \alpha(s's)d_{s'}A_\lambda(xs') \\ &= \lambda \int_a^b A_\lambda(s's)d_{s'}\alpha(xs'). \end{aligned}$$

Associated with (7) we have the equation

$$(8) \qquad \varphi(x) = f(x) - \lambda \int_a^b f(s) d_s A_\lambda(xs),$$

and the theorem:

THEOREM. *If $\alpha(xs)$ is continuous in x for every value of s and x, and is of uniformly limited variation in s for x in ab, and if $f(x)$ is continuous in ab, then (2) has one and only one continuous solution, and it may be written in the form (8), provided λ is taken small enough $(\leqq 1/T_a)$.*

In fact, (8) follows from (2) by (7) in the same manner exactly, as in the corresponding theory of the ordinary integral equation;* and vice versa, (2) follows from (8). Hence our problem is reduced to finding a function $A_\lambda(xs)$, continuous in x for every value of s, and of uniformly limited variation in s for x in ab, which satisfies both of the equations (7). This function is given by the formula

$$(9) \qquad A_\lambda(xs) = - \sum_0^\infty \lambda^i \alpha_i(xs),$$

where α_i is the ith iterated kernel:

$$\alpha_i(xs) = \int_a^b \alpha(s's) d_{s'} \alpha_{i-1}(xs'), \qquad i > 0,$$

$$\alpha_0(xs) = \alpha(xs).$$

These last formulæ may be rewritten for $i > 0$, in the form:

$$(9') \quad \alpha_i(xs) = \int_a^b \alpha_j(s's) d_{s'} \alpha_{i-j-1}(xs'), \qquad j = 0, 1, \cdots, i-1,$$

as we see by (6). As is verified by mathematical induction, all these functions are continuous in x for every s; moreover they are all functions of uniformly limited variation in s. We have in fact from (5') the inequality

$$T_{a_i} \leqq (T_a)^{i+1}.$$

* See for instance Bôcher, Introduction to the Study of Integral Equations, Cambridge (Eng.) (1909), pp. 21, 22.

Also, we have from (3) the inequality

$$|\alpha_i(xs)| \leq N|T_a|^i \qquad \text{where} \qquad |\alpha(xs)| \leq N.$$

Hence the series (9) is absolutely and uniformly convergent for x and s in ab, if λ is taken small enough:

$$(10) \qquad\qquad |\lambda| < \frac{1}{T_a}.$$

We know therefore that $A_\lambda(xs)$ is continuous in x for every value of s.

It remains to point out that $A_\lambda(xs)$ is a function of uniformly limited variation in s. We know however that if a series of functions of limited variation, $\Sigma\varphi_i(x)$, has a limit $\varphi(x)$, and converges in such a way that the series of positive constants ΣT_{ϕ_i} also converges, then the convergence is uniform, and $\varphi(x)$ is a function of limited variation; moreover

$$T_\phi \leq \Sigma T_{\phi_i}.$$

We have then the inequality

$$T_A \leq \frac{T_a}{1 - \lambda T_a},$$

and the point is proved.

With the hypotheses given above, we cannot develop the Fredholm theory of the equation (2). It is not difficult to add the additional necessary postulate,* but rather than introduce artificiality into this treatment, which is so far closely related to its intuitional basis, let us turn to other points of view.

§ 2. The General Analysis of E. H. Moore

63. Possible Points of View. The theory of the linear integral equation

$$u(x) = \varphi(x) + \int_a^b K(x\xi)u(\xi)d\xi$$

* To enable us to deal with the function

$$\lim_{n=\infty} \sum_0^n \{\alpha(\xi_i s_i) - \alpha(\xi_i s_{i-1})\}.$$

admits of two types of direct generalization. On the one hand, by paying attention to the formal nature of the demonstrations involved in the theory, the variables, functions and linear operations involved may be generalized to the fullest extent that would enable them still to satisfy the same formal relations; on the other hand, by noticing the combinatorial properties of the operations which produce the iterated kernels, a calculus of these combinations may be created, and the theory extended far beyond the realms of linearity. The first of these methods has yielded, in the hands of Professor E. H. Moore, chapters of his *General Analysis*; the second has produced Volterra's theory of *Permutable Functions*.

In the original theory of integral equations the domain of the independent variable was the linear continuum. It was noticed immediately that the theory was independent of dimension, and could be generalized at once to n dimensions and n-tple integrals, even to systems of such equations. Further than this, E. H. Moore has shown that considerations of order in general, in the domain of the independent variable, are immaterial. The method of successive approximation, the Fredholm method, and the Hilbert-Schmidt method involve no hypothesis whatever with respect to this domain. This fact itself gives an indication of the importance and basic nature of the theory of integral equations.

The essential nature of the theory may be obtained by noticing the analogies in theories that relate to diverse subjects, proceeding according to Professor Moore's dictum, "The existence of analogies between central features of various theories implies the existence of a general theory which underlies the particular theories and unifies them with respect to those central features," or we may merely make an abstraction of the formal nature of a single given development, and define the properties of abstract elements by postulates sufficient to produce the desired results. The latter is the method used by Russell in his "Principles of Mathematics." In fact, the General Analysis of E. H. Moore may be considered as an additional chapter in that treatment of mathematics.

The "General Analysis" constitutes a treatise on the abstract relations and classes of general variables, sufficient to afford in their properties, analogies with the usual analysis based on linear or multiply-dimensional continuous point sets.* In this lecture we consider merely the portion of that theory directly related to the theory of integral equations. We use of course the notation of Professor Moore.

64. The Linear Equation and its Kernel. The equation to be considered is the following:

$$(G) \qquad \xi = \eta - z J \kappa \eta$$

or, more explicitly,

$$\xi(s) = \eta(s) - z J_t \kappa(st) \eta(t),$$

in which κ is called the kernel, and η is the function to be determined; J_t is a functional operation turning a product $\kappa \eta$ or $\kappa(st)\eta(t)$ into a function of the argument s, whose defining postulates will be given later; ξ and η are themselves functions of an argument s or t, the argument having a range or domain $\mathfrak{P}$; and the equation G holds for every s of the range $\mathfrak{P}$.

The range $\mathfrak{P}$ is not necessarily a linear continuum, or multiply dimensional continuum, or point set,—although so far as I know, no applications have been given where the range is of necessity more general. The elements p of $\mathfrak{P}$ may be numbers, functions, points, curves; moreover for part of the range the elements may be of one sort, and for part, of another. Thus, the equation (G) contains as special cases, the equations

$$(I) \qquad x = y - zky,$$

$$(II_n) \qquad x_i = y_i - z \sum_1^n {}_j k_{ij} y_j, \qquad i = 1, 2, \cdots, n,$$

$$(III) \qquad x_i = y_i - z \sum_1^\infty {}_j k_{ij} y_j, \qquad i = 1, 2, \cdots,$$

$$(IV) \qquad \xi(s) = \eta(s) - z \int_a^b \kappa(st)\eta(t)dt, \qquad a \leq s \leq b,$$

---

* New Haven Mathematical Colloquium, New Haven (1910). See also the citation of Professor Moore on which this lecture is based, and summaries by G. D. Birkhoff, *Bulletin of the American Mathematical Society*, vol. 17 (1911), p. 414, and by O. Bolza, *Jahresbericht der deutschen Mathematiker-Vereinigung*, vol. 23 (1914), p. 248.

and the task of the analysis is to devise a system of postulates which will make the results in these cases merely specializations of the general results for equation (G). The methods used will be clear to anyone who is familiar with the usual analysis of equations (III) and (IV).

The connection established between (III) and (IV) is by means of *relatively uniform convergence*. A sequence of functions μ_n, $n = 1, 2, \cdots$, on the range $\mathfrak{P}$ converges *uniformly* to a limit function θ, *relatively* to a scale function σ,

$$\lim_{n=\infty} \mu_n = \theta, \qquad (\mathfrak{P}; \sigma),$$

provided that n_0 can be found, so that given e the following inequality will be satisfied:

$$|\mu_n(p) - \theta(p)| \leq e|\sigma(p)|, \quad n \geq n_0.$$

It is also convenient to be able to speak of *relative uniformity as to a class $\mathfrak{S}$ of scale functions*:

$$\lim_{n=\infty} \mu_n = \theta, \qquad (\mathfrak{P}; \mathfrak{S}),$$

when any member of the class may be found which will serve as a scale function.

65. Bases and Postulates for Equation (G). In order to obtain a theory for the equation (G) we must arrange a *basis* of classes of functions related one to another with reference to the possibility of performing the operation J, and also certain limiting operations of successive approximation. Thus with reference to this equation we may postulate the basis

$$(11) \qquad \Sigma_4 = (\mathfrak{A}; \mathfrak{P}; \mathfrak{M}; \mathfrak{N} \equiv \mathfrak{M}_*{}^2; \mathfrak{R} \equiv (\mathfrak{M}\mathfrak{M})_*; J),$$

which we now proceed to explain.

In the scheme (11), which is merely a shorthand method of remembering what classes of functions we are dealing with, $\mathfrak{A}$ denotes the class of all real or all complex numbers, as we choose; $\mathfrak{P}$ denotes the domain of the variable in the general significance already mentioned; $\mathfrak{M}$ is the class of functions $\mu(p)$, of the variable p in $\mathfrak{P}$, to which the functions η and ξ of equation (G) belong; $\mathfrak{N}$ is the class of functions of t on which the operation J may be performed; and finally, $\mathfrak{R}$ denotes the class of functions to which the kernel function $\kappa(st)$ of (G) must belong.

The significance of the equations

(12) $$\mathfrak{N} \equiv \mathfrak{M}_*{}^2$$

and

(13) $$\mathfrak{R} \equiv (\mathfrak{M}\mathfrak{M})_*$$

may now be made clear. The symbol $\mathfrak{M}^2$ denotes the class of product functions $\mu_1(p)\mu_2(p)$ of a single variable, of which the factors are functions of $\mathfrak{M}$. On the other hand, the symbol $(\mathfrak{M}\mathfrak{M})$ denotes the class of product functions $\mu_1(p_1)\mu_2(p_2)$ of two variables, of which the factors are functions of $\mathfrak{M}$; in this latter case, p_1 and p_2 are independent variables, each one ranging over $\mathfrak{P}$.

A symbol $\mathfrak{M}_*$ denotes the class of functions obtained by adding to $\mathfrak{M}$, first the functions

$$\bar{\mu} = a_1\mu_1 + a_2\mu_2 + \cdots + a_n\mu_n,$$

the functions μ_i being arbitrary functions of $\mathfrak{M}$, and the coefficients a_i being arbitrary numbers from $\mathfrak{A}$ (i. e., arbitrary real or complex numbers as the case may be), thus forming the class designated as $\mathfrak{M}_L$, and second, the functions

(14) $$\mu_p = \lim_{i=\infty} \bar{\mu}_i,$$

where $\{\bar{\mu}_i\}$ is a sequence of functions $\bar{\mu}$ which converges uniformly to μ_p over $\mathfrak{P}$, relatively to a scale function which must be taken from $\mathfrak{M}_L$. It can easily be shown that if $\mathfrak{M}$ possesses the property (D), given below, then $\mathfrak{M}_L$ and $\mathfrak{M}_*$ possess the same property, and uniform convergence relative to the class $\mathfrak{M}$ is the same as that relative to $\mathfrak{M}_L$ or $\mathfrak{M}_*$. Moreover $(\mathfrak{M}_*)_* = \mathfrak{M}_*$.

Hence the significance of (12) is that $\mathfrak{N}$ is the totality of functions $\nu(t)$ such that

(12') $$\nu(t) = \lim_{i=\infty} \nu_i(t), \qquad (\mathfrak{P}; \mathfrak{M}^2),$$

where $\{\nu_i(t)\}$ is a sequence of functions

$$\nu_i(t) = a_{i1}\bar{\mu}_{i1}(t)\mu_{i1}(t) + a_{i2}\bar{\mu}_{i2}(t)\mu_{i2}(t) + \cdots + a_{in}\bar{\mu}_{in}(t)\mu_{in}(t),$$

the functions $\bar{\mu}_{ij}$ and μ_{ij} being arbitrary functions from $\mathfrak{M}$, and the coefficients a_{ij} arbitrary numbers from $\mathfrak{A}$. The convergence, as is indicated, is uniform over $\mathfrak{P}$, relatively to some scale function which is the product of two functions of $\mathfrak{M}$. Similarly, the significance of (13) is that $\mathfrak{R}$ is the totality of functions $\kappa(st)$ such that

(13') $$\kappa(st) = \lim_{i=\infty} \nu_i(st),$$

where $\{\nu_i(st)\}$ is a sequence of functions

$$\nu_i(st) = \sum_{1}^{n_i}{}_j a_{ij}\bar{\mu}_{ij}(s)\mu_{ij}(t).$$

The convergence is uniform over the range $(\mathfrak{P}\mathfrak{P})$ (i. e., the range of the composite variable s, t) relatively to some function $\bar{\mu}(s)\mu(t)$, as a scale function.

All of the description of the basis, just given, is implied by the array (11). In order to develop the complete analysis of the equation (G) it is necessary merely to specify certain postulates which are to hold for the class of functions $\mathfrak{M}$, and the operation J.

As to the class of functions $\mathfrak{M}$, the postulates must be four, (L), (C), (D_0) and (D) as follows:

(L) If $\mu_1, \cdots, \mu_n$ are functions of $\mathfrak{M}$, and $a_1, \cdots, a_n$ elements of $\mathfrak{A}$, then $a_1\mu_1 + \cdots + a_n\mu_n$ is a function of $\mathfrak{M}$.

(C) If $\{\mu_n\}$ represents a sequence of functions of $\mathfrak{M}$, then the limit

$$\mu = \lim_{n=\infty} \mu_n, \qquad (\mathfrak{P}; \mathfrak{M})$$

is a function of $\mathfrak{M}$, provided that the convergence is uniform relatively to a scale function of $\mathfrak{M}$.

(D_0) If μ is a function of $\mathfrak{M}$, there must be some real-valued nowhere-negative function μ_0 (which may vary with μ) of $\mathfrak{M}$, such that for every p of $\mathfrak{P}$

$$|\mu(p)| \leq \mu_0(p).$$

(*D*) If $\{\mu_n\}$ represents a sequence of functions of $\mathfrak{M}$, there must be a function μ of $\mathfrak{M}$, and a sequence of numbers $\{a_n\}$ of $\mathfrak{A}$ such that for every p of $\mathfrak{P}$

$$|\mu_n(p)| \leq |a_n\mu(p)|, \qquad n = 1, 2, \cdots.$$

The postulates (*L*) and (*C*) together may be stated by saying that

$$\mathfrak{M} \equiv \mathfrak{M}_*.$$

The operation J must satisfy two postulates (*L*) and (*M*), as follows:

(*L*) If J operates on a class of functions $\mathfrak{N}$, and ν, ν_1, ν_2 are three functions of $\mathfrak{N}$ such that $\nu = a_1\nu_1 + a_2\nu_2$, then

$$J(\nu) = a_1 J(\nu_1) + a_2 J(\nu_2).$$

(*M*) There exists a functional operation M (called a *modulus*) on real-valued nowhere-negative functions ν_0 of $\mathfrak{N}$ such that $M(\nu_0)$ is a real non-negative number, for which a relation $|\nu(p)| \leq \nu_0(p)$ holding for every p of $\mathfrak{P}$ implies the relation $|J(\nu)| \leq M(\nu_0)$.

These postulates suffice to prove the fundamental properties of the obvious generalizations of the Fredholm determinants and minors, familiar in the theory of the linear integral equation of the second kind. There exists a resolvent kernel λ to κ which is the ratio of two integral functions of the parameter z, the denominator depending on z alone, and not on s, t, such that the relation (the Volterra relation)

$$(15) \qquad \kappa(st) + \lambda(st) = z\,J_u\kappa(su)\lambda(ut) = z\,J_u\lambda(su)\kappa(ut)$$

is satisfied. Hence unless z is a root of κ (i. e., a value which makes vanish the denominator of λ) there is one and only one solution of (*G*); it has moreover the form:

$$(16) \qquad \eta = \xi - z\,J\lambda\xi.$$

Rather than proceed into details which will be trivial to those familiar with the theory of integral equation, let us follow Professor Moore in some fundamental generalizations.

66. The Equation (G^5). The equation (G) with the significance

$$(G^5) \qquad \xi(s) = \eta(s) - z J_{tu}\kappa(st)\eta(u)$$

is suggested by the integral equation of the second kind, when the
integral is iterated instead of simple. Thus in the above equation, we might have as a special case:

$$J_{tu}\kappa(st)\eta(u) \equiv \int_a^b dt\kappa(st) \int_a^b \omega(tu)\eta(u)du,$$

the ω being implicitly a part of the definition, in this case. What
makes (G^5) important however is that it possesses a certain
closure property (called by Moore *the closure property* C_2);*
namely, if it is attempted to generalize (G_5) by the same sort of
process by means of which (G^5) was itself suggested, nothing
new is obtained. The operation

$$J_{tuvw}\kappa(stuv)\eta(w),$$

with its postulates, is reducible by a mere renaming of the general
variables to the operation in equation (G^5) and its postulates.
In this sense, *the equation* (G^5) *contains its own generalization.*

Since in (G^5) the J is an operation on functions of two variables
t, u or p_1, p_2, the class $\mathfrak{N}$ must be related to $\mathfrak{M}$ in a different way
than in Σ_4. In the basis which is called Σ_5 by Moore, the
class $\mathfrak{N}$ becomes the class $(\mathfrak{M}\mathfrak{M})_* \equiv \mathfrak{N}$. Hence we may write
the basis

(17) $\qquad \Sigma_5 = (\mathfrak{A}; \mathfrak{P}; \mathfrak{M}; \mathfrak{N} \equiv (\mathfrak{M}\mathfrak{M})_*; J \text{ on } \mathfrak{N} \text{ to } \mathfrak{A}),$

with the postulates (L), (C), (D_0), (D) for $\mathfrak{M}$ and the postulates
(L), (M) for J; or the same situation may be stated by the
basis

$$(\mathfrak{A}; \mathfrak{P}; \mathfrak{M} \equiv \mathfrak{M}_*; \mathfrak{N} \equiv (\mathfrak{M}\mathfrak{M})_*; J \text{ on } \mathfrak{N} \text{ to } \mathfrak{A}),$$

with the postulates (D_0), (D) for $\mathfrak{M}$, and the postulates (L), (M)
for J. By putting $u = t$ the equation (G^5) reduces to the equation (G) with its earlier significance, and the basis Σ_5 to Σ_4.

---

* Moore interprets this closure property in terms of generalized scalar
(inner) products, which form the "skeleton" of the class $\mathfrak{K}$.

It is to be noted that the equation (G^5), with the postulates imposed, encloses as special cases the equations (I), (II$_n$), (III), (IV) with the assumptions usually made for those theories.* This property is called *the closure property* C_1.

67. The Closure Properties C_3 and C_4. The equation in the significance (G^5) is its own generalization also from other points of view. Thus if we consider a set of n simultaneous equations

$$(18) \qquad \xi_i(s) = \eta_i(s) - z \sum_{1}^{n} {}_j J_{tu} \kappa_{ij}(st) \eta_j(u)$$

all on the same basis Σ_5, or on different bases Σ_5^i, $i = 1, 2, \cdots, n$, they may be replaced by a single equation (G^5) on a new basis Σ_5, formed by compounding the old ones in the manner familiar in the theory of integral equations. The range $\mathfrak{P}$ of the new Σ_5 is the logical sum of the ranges $\mathfrak{P}_i$ of the $\Sigma_5^{(i)}$, and a function θ on this $\mathfrak{P}$ determines a function θ_i on each of the ranges $\mathfrak{P}_i$.† The range $\mathfrak{P}\mathfrak{P}$ becomes therefore the logical sum of the n^2 product ranges $\mathfrak{P}_i\mathfrak{P}_j$, etc.

The closure property specified in the preceding paragraph, indicated as C_3, is equivalent to the passage from (I) to (II$_n$). On account of the lack of necessity for postulates of order in the domain of the independent variable, this generalization when applied to (G^5) yields, as we have said, merely another equation (G^5). A further type of self-contained generalization, by what Moore calls **-composition*, constitutes *the closure property* C_4. This ingenious generalization is suggested by that from Σ_4 to Σ_5 or perhaps from a basis of (I) to Σ_5.

Given the system of bases Σ^i, with a common class $\mathfrak{A}$, the composite basis $\Sigma_{1\ldots n^*}$ is determined as follows. The class $\mathfrak{A}$ of Σ^* is the common $\mathfrak{A}$ for the Σ^i; the range $\mathfrak{P}$ for Σ^* is the range in n variables given as the product range of $\mathfrak{P}_1, \cdots, \mathfrak{P}_i$. The class $\mathfrak{M}$ on $\mathfrak{P}$ is the class of the functions of n variables

$$\mathfrak{M} \equiv (\mathfrak{M}_1\mathfrak{M}_2\cdots\mathfrak{M}_n)_*,$$

---

* A detailed exposition of this closure property is given in the paper by O. Bolza already cited.

† The ranges $\mathfrak{P}_i$ need not of course be distinct. The range $\mathfrak{P}_1$, for instance, may consist merely of a subset of elements from the range $\mathfrak{P}_2$.

and the class $\Re$ on the range $\mathfrak{P}\mathfrak{P}$ is the class of functions of $2n$ variables

$$\Re = (\Re_1 \Re_2 \cdots \Re_n)_*.$$

As for the operation J, that is let become of the type of an iterated operation

$$J_\kappa = J_1 J_2 \cdots J_n \kappa.$$

The postulates of Art. 66 holding for each of the bases Σ^i imply the same postulates for the new basis $\Sigma_{1 \cdots n*}$, and thus the new equation as developed is merely an instance of the original (G^5).

Numerous instances suggest themselves. As a special case, (G^5) contains the equation

$$(19) \quad \begin{aligned} \xi(s_1 \cdots s_n) &= \eta(s_1 \cdots s_n) \\ &- z J'_{t_1 u_1} \cdots J^{(n)}_{t_n u_n} \kappa(s_1 \cdots s_n, t_1 \cdots t_n) \eta(u_1 \cdots u_n). \end{aligned}$$

If the basis for (II_n) is combined with the basis for (G^5), the resulting equation is as follows:*

$$(20) \quad \xi(is) = \eta(is) - z \sum_1^n {}_j J_{tu} \kappa(isjt) \eta(ju), \qquad i = 1, 2, \cdots, n;$$

and if the basis for (III) is combined with that for (G^5) there results a theory of the infinite system of equations

$$\xi(is) = \eta(is) - z \sum_1^\infty {}_j J_{tu} \kappa(isjt) \eta(ju), \qquad i = 1, 2, 3, \cdots.$$

This obviously contains as a special case a theory for an infinite system of linear differential equations, in an infinite number of unknowns and one independent variable.

68. Mixed Linear Equations. A practical consequence of the closure property C_3 is that (G^5) contains as a special case the mixed linear equation; in particular, the mixed linear *integral* equation, treated most significantly by W. A. Hurwitz.† This

---

* Equation (20) appears also under the closure property C_3.

† W. A. Hurwitz, *Transactions of the American Mathematical Society*, vol. 16 (1915), pp. 121–133.

equation may be studied in the form

$$(21) \qquad \xi = \eta - z \sum_1^n {}_j J_j \kappa_j \eta,$$

where the ranges $\mathfrak{P}_j$ may be taken as identical. In E. H. Moore's treatment this equation is taken as an example of a system of equations of the form (18), where the n equations are identical. It is therefore a special case of the equation (G^5).

The *adjoint* of (G^5), which may be conveniently studied with it, is the equation

$$(22) \qquad \bar{\xi}(t) = \bar{\eta}(t) - z J_{rs} \kappa(st) \eta(r).$$

In the case of the equation (21) the adjoint is therefore a whole system of equations; it is moreover of the character specified by Hurwitz. In order however to obtain completely the form given by Hurwitz it would be necessary to generalize his theory of the *pseudo resolvent*.*

69. Further Developments. In the equation (G^5) the class $\mathfrak{R}$ of the functions κ has been defined over the range $\mathfrak{P}\mathfrak{P}$. It is pointed out by Moore that there is no reason why s and t in $\kappa(st)$ should have the same range. In fact, if the range of the functions of $\mathfrak{M}$ is $\mathfrak{P}$, the range of the functions of $\mathfrak{R}$ may be $\mathfrak{P}\bar{\mathfrak{P}}$, where $\bar{\mathfrak{P}}$ is independent of $\mathfrak{P}$. This is the furthest point to which the generalization of the Fredholm theory, that is, the theory of the integral equation of the second kind, is carried.

This last form of generalization is impossible for the theory of the integral equation of the first kind (the Hilbert-Schmidt theory). Here the basis Σ_5 must be adhered to, and it is necessary to introduce the characteristic postulate of the symmetry of $\kappa(st)$ if $\kappa(st)$ is real, or, if $\kappa(st)$ is complex, that $\kappa(ts)$ shall be the conjugate complex quantity to $\kappa(st)$.

It is obvious that many theories may be amalgamated with the developments of this generalization. Thus some of the theory of linear and non-linear differential equations, and the theory of permutable functions may be so translated. Such generalizations are useful, but are apt to be somewhat facile.

* W. A. Hurwitz, *ibid.*, vol. 13 (1912), p. 408.

The consequence of specialization of the range of the general variable, say by the introduction of concepts like that of distance,* is however the subject of fruitful study.

70. The Content of the Operation J. So far the operation J has been defined by postulates, and not explicitly. In order to get some idea of its generality for a given range of the general variable, let us choose the range as the most familiar one, namely, the one-dimensional continuum. Let us assume that the class $\mathfrak{M}$ contains (or can be extended by definition to contain) the totality of continuous functions over this range, which we may take to be the interval ab. *In this case, the operation is merely a Stieltjes integral*:

$$(23) \qquad J_{tu}\kappa(st)\eta(u) = \int_a^b \eta(t)d_t\alpha(st).$$

In fact from the dominance property (D_0) and the modular property (M) it follows that if s is given a constant value s_0, and $|\eta(t)| < 1$, then there is a constant C_{s_0} such that

$$\left| J_{tu}\kappa(s_0t)\eta(u) \right| < C_{s_0}.$$

Hence for every η it follows by the linearity property (L) that the inequality

$$(24) \qquad \left| J_{tu}\kappa(st)\eta(u) \right| < C_s \max_a^b |\eta|$$

is satisfied. This and the linearity property constitute the two Riesz conditions of Art. 40, and our statement is therefore proved.

We may express $\alpha(st)$ directly in terms of $\kappa(st)$. Either side of (23) is a linear functional of η, which we may denote by

$$T[\eta]._a^b$$

---

* Besides the references to Moore, see papers by Fréchet, and Pitcher, e. g., Pitcher, *American Journal of Mathematics*, vol. 36 (1914), pp. 261–266, where the literature is given. The fundamental memoir on this subject is Fréchet's Thesis, already cited.

If now, as in Lecture III, equation (23), we define

$$f_{u_1u_2} = 1, \qquad u_1 < u \le u_2,$$
$$= 0, \qquad \text{otherwise, etc.,}$$

and also define the new symbol

(25) $$\overset{u_2}{\underset{u_1}{J}}_{tu\kappa}(st) = T[\overset{b}{\underset{a}{f}}_{u_1u_2}], \qquad \overset{u_2}{\underset{a}{J}}_{tu\kappa}(st) = T[\overset{b}{\underset{a}{f}}_{au_2}],$$

then we have

(26) $$\alpha(su_2) - \alpha(su_1) = \overset{u_2}{\underset{u_1}{J}}_{tu\kappa}(st), \qquad \alpha(su_2) = \overset{u_2}{\underset{a}{J}}_{tu\kappa}(st),$$

which gives us α in terms of κ.

Let us now divide the interval ab into sub-intervals by points $a = u_0, u_1, \cdots, u_n = b$, and let s_i be a point in the region $u_{i-1} < s_i < u_i$. On account of the continuity of the linear functional, the following equation may be deduced:

(27) $$J_{tu\kappa}(ut) = \lim_{n=\infty} \sum_{1}^{n} {}_i(\alpha(s_iu_i) - \alpha(s_iu_{i-1})).$$

The left-hand member of (27) is one of the constituents of the Fredholm determinant, corresponding to $\int_a^b \kappa(tt)dt$ in the theory of integral equations.*

§ 3. The Theory of Permutable Functions, and Combinations of Integrals

71. The Associative Combinations of the First and Second Kinds. In this second form of generalization of the theory of integral equations, what is of primary importance is an associative combination of integrals. In fact, Volterra's theory rests upon the identity

(28) $$\int_a^b ds_1 K_1(rs_1) \int_a^b K_2(s_1s_2)K_3(s_2s)ds_2$$
$$= \int_a^b \left[\int_a^b K_1(rs_1)K_2(s_1s_2)ds_1 \right] K_3(s_2s)ds_2,$$

* See footnote at end of Art. 62.

and as a special case, putting $K_i(rs) = 0$ when $s > r$,

$$
\begin{aligned}
(29) \quad \int_s^r ds_1 K_1(rs_1) \int_s^{s_1} K_2(s_1 s_2) K_3(s_2 s) ds_2 \\
= \int_s^r \left[\int_{s_2}^r K_1(rs_1) K_2(s_1 s_2) ds_1 \right] K_3(s_2 s) ds_2.
\end{aligned}
$$

This last equation is sometimes called *Dirichlet's formula*,[*] and may of course be established directly.   If we define

$$
(30) \qquad K_1 K_2 = \int_a^b K_1(rs_1) K_2(s_1 s) ds_1
$$

or

$$
(31) \qquad K_1 K_2 = \int_s^r K_1(rs_1) K_2(s_1 s) ds_1,
$$

which are respectively the combinations of the second and first kinds, we shall have by (28) and (29) the equation

$$
(32) \qquad K_1(K_2 K_3) = (K_1 K_2) K_3,
$$

which is the *associative law* for these symbolic products.[†]

The hypothesis of commutativity, if it is made,

$$
(33) \qquad K_1 K_2 = K_2 K_1,
$$

is Volterra's *condition of permutability*.[‡]   *If two functions are permutable with a third, they are permutable with each other.*[§]

[*] U. Dini, Lezioni di analisi infinitesimale, Pisa, vol. 2, p. 925.

[†] In terms of Moore's General Analysis, if in (G^5) we introduce a parameter r, we may regard $J_{tu}\kappa(st)\eta(ur)$ as a symbolic product of the functions $\kappa(sr)$ and $\eta(sr)$.   If we restrict ourselves to the same operation J and class $\mathfrak{M}$, and various kernels κ, ω, η, etc., the succession of two applications of the operation turns out to be commutative (see the article by Moore on which this lecture is based, also Hildebrand, *Transactions of the American Mathematical Society*, vol. 18 (1917), pp. 73–96).   Hence the triple product $\kappa\omega\eta$ is associative, and the theory of Volterra's generalization may be extended to the General Analysis.

[‡] Volterra, *Rendiconti della R. Acc. dei Lincei*, vol. 19 (1910), 1st sem., pp. 169–180.

[§] Vessiot, *Comptes Rendus*, vol. 154 (1912), pp. 682–684.   A comprehensive study of permutable functions, with special reference to the case when the functions are analytic in r and s has been given by J. Pérès, Sur les fonctions permutables de première espèce de M. Vito Volterra, Thèse, no. d'ordre: 1567, Paris (1915).

72. The Algebra of Permutable and Non-Permutable Functions.

In order to facilitate the inverse operation corresponding to division, we abandon slightly Volterra's notation and introduce complex quantities

$$\kappa = k + jK(rs),$$
$$\xi = u + jU(rs),$$

etc., where k and u are constants, and K and U are functions of r, s as indicated. We say that $\kappa = \xi$ if $k = u$ and $K(rs) \equiv U(rs)$, and define the zero element and the addition and subtraction of elements in the usual way. In the quantity κ we speak of k as the *ordinary coefficient* and $K(rs)$ as the *functional coefficient*; and if the ordinary coefficient vanishes we speak of κ as a *function of nullity*. Both k and K may contain extra parameters $x, y, \cdots$, which do not enter into the functional operation, now to be described.

We define the product

$$(34) \quad \kappa\xi = ku + j\{kU(rs) + uK(rs) + \int K(rs_1)U(s_1s)ds_1\},$$

where the integral sign denotes the combination of the first or second kind according to the algebra we are treating; if necessary to distinguish between these two products we may denote them by $[\kappa\xi]_1$ and $[\kappa\xi]_2$ respectively, or make use of the symbols $\int_1 KU, \int_2 KU, \int_1 U^n$, etc. Generally, we shall not need to impose a condition of permutability on the functions involved, and so we shall be using an algebra which does not contain the commutative property. The associative law for multiplication is however always satisfied, as well as the distributive.

We shall have both left-handed and right-handed division. In the algebra of the first kind, division by a function κ, not of nullity, is equivalent, by the definition of equality, to first an ordinary division (to satisfy the relation among the ordinary coefficients), and second, the resolution of an integral equation of the second kind of Volterra type. This resolution is always possible and unique, provided that the functions are finite

$(|K(rs)| \leqq M_K)$, and continuous. In order to obtain the same unique result in the algebra of the second kind (which depends upon solving a Fredholm equation), we assume that every functional coefficient $K(rs)$ or $U(rs)$ contains a parameter, say λ, in such a way that the inequality

(35) $$|K(rs)| \leqq \lambda M_K, \qquad M_K \text{ a constant,}$$

is satisfied; and we consider values of λ in the neighborhood of $\lambda = 0$ $(|\lambda| < k/(b - a)M_K)$.*

The idemfactor exists in both algebras, and has the value $1 + j0$. If we do not make the assumption of permutability, all the laws of algebra are satisfied except the commutative law, with the proviso that division by a function of nullity corresponds to division by zero.† *If we make the assumption of permutability, the results of the algebraic operations yield again permutable functions, and all the laws of elementary algebra are satisfied; in fact the symbolic algebra of the quantities κ, ξ, $\cdots$ is isomorphic with the algebra of their ordinary coefficients, k, u, $\cdots$.*

In particular, we can apply to these generalized integral equations the theory of Lagrange. The equations of degrees 1, 2, 3, 4 can be solved by making use of binomial equations as resolvents.‡

73. The Volterra Relation and Reciprocal Functions. The Volterra relation is that which holds between a given kernel and the kernel of the resolvent integral equation, and may be written in the form

(36) $$K(rs) + K'(rs) = \int KK'.$$

---

* Or values of λ which are not special parameter values for the functions concerned. See C. E. Seely, Certain Non-Linear Integral Equations, Dissertation, Lancaster (1914).

† See for instance Huntington, *Annals of Mathematics*, 2d series, vol. 8 (1906). Compare with the expressions on pages 134, 135.

‡ The solution of binomial equations depends upon expansion in series; see Art. 75, below.

The functions K and K' we shall speak of as *reciprocal*; they will be permutable. If now, we write

(37) $$\kappa = 1 - jK(rs), \qquad \kappa' = 1 - jK'(rs),$$

equation (36) takes on the special form

(37') $$\kappa\kappa' = 1.$$

On account of the permutability of K and K' we have also

$$\kappa'\kappa = 1.$$

Let us, by putting a bar over a function, denote the function reciprocal to it. The formula for division in general may be expressed simply, in terms of this notation. In fact, we have

(38)
$$\frac{1}{u + jU(rs)} = \frac{1}{u}\left(\frac{1}{1 - j\left\{ -\dfrac{1}{u} U(rs) \right\}} \right)$$

$$= \frac{1}{u} - j\frac{1}{u}\overline{\left(-\frac{1}{u} U(rs) \right)}.$$

Moreover by writing (36) in the form

$$jK(rs) + j\overline{K}(rs) = jK(rs)j\overline{K}(rs)$$

we get the formula

(38') $$j\overline{K}(rs) = \frac{-jK(rs)}{1 - jK(rs)}.$$

Let $U_1 \cdots U_m$ be continuous functions of r, s, permutable among themselves or not, and let $\overline{U}_1, \cdots, \overline{U}_m$ be the reciprocal functions. Then the functions U and V, defined by the equations

(39)
$$jU = 1 - (1 - jU_1)^{p_1}(1 - j\overline{U}_1)^{q_1}\cdots(1 - jU_m)^{p_m}(1 - j\overline{U}_m)^{q_m},$$
$$jV = 1 - (1 - jU_m)^{q_m}(1 - j\overline{U}_m)^{p_m}\cdots(1 - jU_1)^{q_1}(1 - j\overline{U}_1)^{p_1},$$

where the p_i, q_i are arbitrary integers, positive or negative, are reciprocal functions. In fact it may be at once verified that we have

$$(1 - jU)(1 - jV) = (1 - jV)(1 - jU) = 1.$$

In particular, *if $K_1(rs)$ and $K_2(rs)$ are two continuous functions, and $\overline{K}_1$ and $\overline{K}_2$ are their reciprocal functions, then the functions*

(40)
$$K(rs) = K_1(rs) + K_2(rs) - \int K_1(rs_1)K_2(s_1s)ds_1,$$
$$\overline{K}(rs) = \overline{K}_1(rs) + \overline{K}_2(rs) - \int \overline{K}_2(rs_1)\overline{K}_1(s_1s)ds_1$$

are reciprocal.

This theorem has some interesting special cases. If we take $K_1 = U$ and $K_2 = - U$, we get from (40):

$$K(rs) = \int U(rs_1)U(s_1s)ds_1,$$
$$\overline{K}(rs) = \overline{U}(rs) + \overline{(- U(rs))} - \int \overline{U}(rs_1)\overline{(- U(s_1s))}ds_1.$$

But if we form $j\overline{U}j\overline{(- U)}$ by (38'), we have

$$\int \overline{U}(rs_1)\overline{(- U(s_1s))}ds_1 = \overline{\left(\int U(rs_1)U(s_1s)ds_1 \right)} = \overline{K}(rs),$$

and combining this with the previous result, we find that *the reciprocal function to $\int U(rs_1)U(s_1s)ds_1$ is $\frac{1}{2}\{\overline{U}(rs) + \overline{(- U(rs))}\}$.*

If K_1 and K_2 are orthogonal, i. e., if $\int K_1K_2 = 0$, equation (38') tells us that $\overline{K}_1$ and $\overline{K}_2$ are orthogonal. Hence from (40), if K_1 and K_2 are orthogonal functions, the reciprocal function to $K_1 + K_2$ is $\overline{K}_1 + \overline{K}_2$:†

$$\overline{(K_1 + K_2)} = \overline{K}_1 + \overline{K}_2.$$

If λ is not a root (characteristic value) of K_1 or K_2 (that is, a value for which $\overline{K}_1$ or $\overline{K}_2$ fails to exist) then it is not a root of the function $K_1 + K_2 - \int K_1K_2$.

74. Fredholm's Theorem of Multiplication.   In this article let us disregard temporarily the parameter λ and the condition (35).

---

* This theorem is implied by a remark of Fredholm that the transformations of the form $S_f(\varphi) = \varphi(x) - \int_a^b f(xs)\varphi(s)ds$ form a group, the product transformation $S_F = S_g S_f$ being given by $F = f + g + \int gf$; see the fundamental memoir, *Acta Mathematica*, vol. 27, p. 372.

† Lalesco, Théorie des équations intégrales, Paris (1912), p. 41.

The functions $D(rs)$ and D defined by Fredholm,

$$D(rs) = K(rs) - \int_a^b K\begin{pmatrix} rs_1 \\ ss_1 \end{pmatrix} ds_1$$

(41)
$$+ \frac{1}{2!} \int_a^b \int_a^b K\begin{pmatrix} rs_1s_2 \\ ss_1s_2 \end{pmatrix} ds_1 ds_2 - \cdots,$$

$$D = 1 - \int_a^b K(s_1s_1)ds_1 + \frac{1}{2!} \int_a^b \int_a^b K\begin{pmatrix} s_1s_2 \\ s_1s_2 \end{pmatrix} ds_1 ds_2 - \cdots,$$

serve to express the resolvent kernel in the form

(42)
$$\overline{K}(rs) = -\frac{D(rs)}{D};$$

moreover, if we form the variation δK of K (e. g., $(\partial K/\partial\lambda)d\lambda$), we have the formula*

(43) $$\delta \log D = \int_a^b ds\{\delta K(ss) - \int_a^b \overline{K}(ss_1)\delta K(s_1s)ds_1.$$

This may be written in the form

(43′) $$\delta \log D = \int_a^b \{(1 - j\overline{K})j\delta K\}_{r=s}ds.$$

If we have any two functions $\varphi(rs)$ and $\psi(rs)$, we may verify directly the formula

(44) $$\int_a^b \{j\varphi j\psi\}_{r=s}ds = \int_a^b \{j\psi j\varphi\}_{r=s}ds.$$

Hence (43) may also be written in the form

(43″) $$\delta \log D = \int_a^b \{j\delta K(1 - j\overline{K})\}_{r=s}ds.$$

Consider now the expression (43′) when $K = K_1 + K_2 - \int K_1 K_2$. We have by direct differentiation:

$$\delta K = (1 - jK_1)j\delta K_2 + j\delta K_1(1 - jK_2);$$

* Fredholm, loc. cit., p. 380.

hence (43′) becomes

$$\delta \log D = \int_a^b \{(1 - j\overline{K})(1 - jK_1)j\delta K_2 \\ + (1 - j\overline{K})j\delta K_1(1 - jK_2)\}_{r=s}ds,$$

the last term of which, by (44), may be written

$$\int_a^b \{j\delta K_1(1 - jK_2)(1 - j\overline{K})\}_{r=s}ds.$$

But, by (40), we have

$$1 - j\overline{K} = (1 - j\overline{K}_2)(1 - j\overline{K}_1),$$

and therefore, making this substitution,

$$\delta \log D = \int_a^b \{(1 - j\overline{K}_2)j\delta K_2\}_{r=s}ds + \int_a^b \{j\delta K_1(1 - j\overline{K}_1)\}_{r=s}ds,$$

or, by (43′) and (43″),

$$\delta \log D = \delta \log D_1 + \delta \log D_2.$$

Hence

$$\log. D - \log D_1 D_2 = \text{const.}$$

If we replace K_1 by μK_1 and K_2 by μK_2, and write this equation for $\mu = 0$, we find $D = D_1 = D_2 = 1$, and this constant is zero; therefore for $\mu = 1$ we have

(45) $$D = D_1 D_2,$$

which is Fredholm's *theorem of multiplication*.

If $K(rs)$ is an integral analytic function of a parameter λ, then $D(\lambda)$ and $D(rs\lambda)$ will be integral analytic functions of λ, without regard to (35). The equation (43′) will then take the form

$$\frac{d}{d\lambda} \log D(\lambda) = \int_a^b \left\{ (1 - j\overline{K})j\frac{\partial K}{\partial \lambda} \right\}_{r=s} ds.$$

Hence *if K_1 and K_2 are integral analytic functions of a parameter λ, and $K = K_1 + K_2 - \int K_1 K_2$, then*

(45′) $$D(\lambda) = D_1(\lambda)D_2(\lambda),$$

and

$$D(rs\lambda) = D_2(\lambda)D_1(rs\lambda) + D_1(\lambda)D_2(rs\lambda)$$

(45″)
$$+ \int_a^b D_2(rs_1\lambda)D_1(s_1s\lambda)ds_1.$$

75. Developments in Series. Volterra's fundamental theorem upon the convergence of series of symbolic powers, the combination being of the first or second kind, is that *if the series*

(46)
$$a_0 + a_1z + a_2z^2 + \cdots$$

is convergent for some value of $z \neq 0$, *then the series*

(46′)
$$a_0 + a_1zf(rs) + a_2z^2 \int f(rs_1)f(s_1s)ds_1$$
$$+ a_3z^3 \int\int f(rs_1)f(s_1s_2)f(s_2s)ds_1ds_2 + \cdots,$$

where $f(rs)$ *is any finite continuous function, is convergent for all values of* z, *if the integral combination is of the first kind (variable limits), and for sufficiently small values of* z *if the combination is of the second kind (constant limits).* By means of this theorem, new transcendental functions, with special applications to integro-differential equations, may be defined and treated.

The corresponding theorem for symbolic power series in functions $\xi = u + jU(rs)$ contains this theorem as a special case. For the combination of the second kind, we assume the condition (35).

THEOREM. *Given the power series in* u,

(47)
$$a_0 + a_1u + a_2u^2 + \cdots,$$

convergent for $|u| \leq \rho$, *the symbolic power series*

(47′)
$$a_0 + a_1\xi + a_2\xi^2 + \cdots$$

in which $\xi = u + jU(rs)$ *will be convergent for* $|u| \leq \rho'$, *however large* M_U *may be, provided that* $\rho' < \rho$.

The theorem can be verified at once for combinations of the second kind. In fact, if we choose a positive quantity x so that at the same time, $x > 1$ and $x > |b - a|$, we shall have

$$U(rs) \leqq \lambda x M, \qquad M = M_U,$$
$$|\xi^k| \leqq (\rho' + \lambda x M)^k,$$

and so if $|\lambda| \leqq (\rho - \rho')/x M$, we shall have $|\xi^k| \leqq \rho^k$, and the series will be absolutely convergent (and uniformly with respect to the variables rs).

On the other hand, if the equation is of the first kind, we have

$$|U(rs)| \leqq M, \qquad M = M_U,$$

whence

$$|\xi^k| \leqq P_k,$$

where

$$P_k = \rho'^k + k\rho'^{k-1}M + \cdots + \frac{k!\,\rho'^{k-1}M^i x^{i-1}}{i!\,(i-1)!\,(k-i)!} + \cdots + \frac{M^k x^{k-1}}{(k-1)!},$$

x being greater than $|b - a|$ (the variables r and s are contained between limits a and b). If we choose a ρ'' so that $\rho' < \rho'' < \rho$, the original series will be dominated by the series

$$S = P \sum_{k=1}^{\infty} \frac{P_k}{\rho''^k},$$

where P is some constant.

If we split the expression for P_{k+1} after the $i + 1$st term, we shall have

$$P_{k+1} < \rho' \frac{k+1}{k+1-i} P_k + \frac{Mx(k+1)}{i(i+1)} P_k,$$

as is easily verified. Hence

$$\frac{P_{k+1}}{\rho'' P_k} < \frac{\rho'}{\rho''} + \frac{i}{k+1-i} + \frac{Mx}{\rho''} \frac{k+1}{i^2}.$$

But we can choose i as a function of k so that each of the last two terms vanishes as k becomes infinite,* and therefore

$$\lim_{k=\infty} \frac{P_{k+1}}{\rho'' P_k} < 1,$$

* For example, take i as the nearest integer to $k^{2/3}$.

and the dominating series is convergent. Thus the theorem is proved.

The theorem can now be extended to the case where the coefficients a_k are no longer constants, but may be of the form $a_k + jA_k(rs)$.

THEOREM. *The two series*

$$\alpha_0 + \alpha_1\xi + \alpha_2\xi^2 + \cdots,$$
$$\alpha_0 + \xi\alpha_1 + \xi^2\alpha_2 + \cdots,$$

in which $\alpha_i = a_i + jA_i(rs)$, $\xi = u + jU(rs)$, *are convergent for* $|u| \leqq \rho'$ *(uniformly in rs), however large M_U may be, provided that the series*

$$\alpha_0 + \alpha_1 u + \alpha_2 u^2 + \cdots$$

is convergent for $u = \rho$, *with* $\rho' < \rho$, *and remains finite* $\leqq P$ *for* $u = \rho$ *and r, s arbitrary within ab.*

76. Extension of Analytic Functions. The convergence theorems just obtained enable us to generalize without further proof every analytic function, *together with whatever properties may be established by a comparison of power series.* Thus the relations between sin u, cos u, e^u may be generalized; the addition theorems, the moduli of periodicity, certain integro-differential equations which the functions satisfy may also be written immediately for such functions and for the Θ functions.

We define

(48) $$e^\xi = 1 + \xi + \frac{\xi^2}{2!} + \cdots.$$

This series in the theory of functions of a complex variable is convergent for all values of the variable; hence in the present case, the series (48) is convergent for all values of λ, u, M_U. We have

(49) $$e^{\xi+\eta} = e^\xi e^\eta.$$

(50) $$e^{\xi+2m\pi i} = e^\xi, \qquad m = \pm 1, \pm 2, \cdots.$$

From (49) it follows that e^ξ cannot vanish (identically, of course, in r, s) for any limited function $\xi_0 = u_0 + jU(rs)$. For

$e^{1+j0} \neq 0$, and if we should have $e^{\xi_0} = 0$, then

$$e^\xi = e^{\xi - \xi_0} e^{\xi_0} = 0.$$

From the addition theorem (49) we have

$$e^{u + j U(rs)} = e^u e^{j U(rs)}.$$

Hence if we denote the functional coefficient of e^ξ by $E(u, U)$, we shall have by (49),

$$E(u, U) = e^u E(0, U),$$

where

(51)
$$E(0, U) = U(rs) + \frac{1}{2!} \int U(rs_1) U(s_1 r) ds_1$$
$$+ \frac{1}{3!} \int \int U(rs_1) U(s_1 s_2) U(s_2 s) ds_1 ds_2 + \cdots.$$

We may write

(51')
$$e^\xi = e^u (1 + j E(0, U)).$$

It can be shown that the only modulus of periodicity possessed by e^ξ is the one already given, namely $U_0 = 0$, $u_0 = 2\pi i$. Hence the function $E(0, U)$, considered as a functional of U, has no period. It cannot vanish unless $U = 0$.

If we substitute (51') into the addition theorem (49) we obtain the addition theorem for $E(0, U)$,

(52)
$$E(0, U + V) = E(0, U) + E(0, V)$$
$$+ \int E(0, U(rs_1)) E(0, V(s_1 s)) ds_1.$$

The function $E(0, zU)$, in accordance with (51), was defined by Volterra and considered as a transcendental function of z, with the addition theorem corresponding to (52). It has no period in z and cannot vanish unless $z = 0$. This function sometimes is called the *Volterra transcendental*.

The addition theorem for $E(0, U)$ reduces to the Volterra relation if V is put equal to $- U$. Hence, *given the function U, the two quantities $- E(0, U)$, $- E(0, - U)$ are reciprocal functions.*

The theory of the extended Θ functions depends directly on the theory of the function $E(0, U)$. In fact, we define

$$\vartheta(\xi, \beta) = \sum_{-\infty}^{\infty}{}_{n}e^{n^2\beta + 2n\xi}$$

with $\xi = u + jU(rs)$, $\beta = b + jB(rs)$, and assume the real part of b to be negative.

77. Integro-Differential Equations of Static Type, and Green's Theorem. If we let our functions ξ, etc., contain parameters x, y, $\cdots$, distinct from the variables r, s, and introduce differential operators with regard to these variables, we have the formula

$$\frac{\partial}{\partial x}(\xi_1\xi_2) = \xi_1\frac{\partial \xi_2}{\partial x} + \frac{\partial \xi_1}{\partial x}\xi_2,$$

with or without a hypothesis of permutability. The equations which involve symbolic differentiation formulæ of this sort yield a class of integro-differential equations with the variables of integration distinct from those of differentiation. They may be called of *static type*, since they were first applied to the problem of *static hysteresis*, and the analysis of slow motion.

We may treat the general linear differential expression of this sort. Thus, if we have the expression of the second order

$$(53)\qquad L(\xi) = \alpha_{11}\frac{\partial^2\xi}{\partial x^2} + 2\alpha_{12}\frac{\partial^2\xi}{\partial x\partial y} + \alpha_{22}\frac{\partial^2\xi}{\partial y^2}$$
$$+ \alpha_1\frac{\partial \xi}{\partial x} + \alpha_2\frac{\partial \xi}{\partial y} + \alpha\xi,$$

with

$$\xi = u(xy) + jU(xy\,|\,rs),$$
$$\alpha_{ik} = a_{ik}(xy) + jA_{ik}(xy\,|\,rs), \qquad \text{etc.,}$$

we define the adjoint expression

$$(54)\qquad M(\eta) = \frac{\partial^2\eta}{\partial x^2}\beta_{11} + 2\frac{\partial^2\eta}{\partial x\partial y}\beta_{12} + \frac{\partial^2\eta}{\partial y^2}\beta_{22}$$
$$+ \frac{\partial\eta}{\partial x}\beta_1 + \frac{\partial\eta}{\partial y}\beta_2 + \eta\beta,$$

with

$$\beta_{ij} = \alpha_{ij},$$

(55) $$\beta_1 = 2\frac{\partial \alpha_{11}}{\partial x} + 2\frac{\partial \alpha_{12}}{\partial y} - \alpha_1, \qquad \beta_2 = 2\frac{\partial \alpha_{12}}{\partial x} + 2\frac{\partial \alpha_{22}}{\partial y} - \alpha_2,$$

$$\beta = \frac{\partial^2 \alpha_{11}}{\partial x^2} + 2\frac{\partial^2 \alpha_{12}}{\partial x \partial y} + \frac{\partial^2 \alpha_{22}}{\partial y^2} - \frac{\partial \alpha_1}{\partial x} - \frac{\partial \alpha_2}{\partial y} + \alpha.$$

The formulæ for $M(\eta)$ and its coefficients are the well-known ones for differential equations, except that attention is paid to the order of the factors, to avoid the necessity of a hypothesis of permutability.

If we write

(56)
$$S_1 \equiv \eta\left(\alpha_{11}\frac{\partial \xi}{\partial x} + \alpha_{12}\frac{\partial \xi}{\partial y}\right) - \left(\frac{\partial \eta}{\partial x}\alpha_{11} + \frac{\partial \eta}{\partial y}\alpha_{12}\right)\xi$$
$$+ \eta\left(\alpha_1 - \frac{\partial \alpha_{11}}{\partial x} - \frac{\partial \alpha_{12}}{\partial y}\right)\xi,$$

$$S_2 = \eta\left(\alpha_{12}\frac{\partial \xi}{\partial x} + \alpha_{22}\frac{\partial \xi}{\partial y}\right) - \left(\frac{\partial \eta}{\partial x}\alpha_{12} + \frac{\partial \eta}{\partial y}\alpha_{22}\right)\xi$$
$$+ \eta\left(\alpha_2 - \frac{\partial \alpha_{12}}{\partial x} - \frac{\partial \alpha_{22}}{\partial y}\right)\xi,$$

we have Lagrange's identity:

(57) $$\eta L(\xi) - M(\eta)\xi = \frac{\partial S_1}{\partial x} + \frac{\partial S_2}{\partial y},$$

and Green's theorem:

(58) $$\iint [\eta L(\xi) - M(\eta)\xi]dxdy = \int_c [S_1 \cos x, n + S_2 \cos y, n]ds.$$

The equivalent of this theorem was given first by Volterra for the integro-differential equation appearing as a generalization of Laplace's equation in three dimensions. In two dimensions, the equation is obtained by writing

(59)
$$\alpha_{11} = 1 + jA_{11}(rs), \qquad \alpha_{22} = 1 + jA_{22}(rs),$$
$$\alpha_{12} = \alpha_1 = \alpha_2 = \alpha = 0.$$

The use of a function analogous to the Green's function was also pointed out, based on a particular solution analogous to *log r**.

78. The Method of Particular Solutions. The method of particular solutions may be generalized not only to the integro-differential equations we are now discussing, but also to those where the same variable appears in both differentiation and integration.† Consider however, as an example, the generalization of Laplace's equation which we have already mentioned:

$$(59') \qquad \alpha_{11} \frac{\partial^2 \xi}{\partial x^2} + \alpha_{22} \frac{\partial^2 \xi}{\partial y^2} = 0,$$

which may for combinations of the second kind be written explicitly in the form

$$(59'') \quad \frac{\partial^2 U}{\partial x^2} + \frac{\partial^2 U}{\partial y^2} + \int_a^b \left\{ A_{11}(rt) \frac{\partial^2 U(xy \mid ts)}{\partial x^2} + A_{22}(rt) \frac{\partial^2 U(xy \mid ts)}{\partial y^2} \right\} dt = 0.$$

We proceed to obtain the solution of this equation, of form $jU(xy \mid rs)$, which vanishes when $x = 0$, when $x = c$, and when $y = d$, and takes on the values

$$U(x0 \mid rs) = f(xrs)$$

when $y = 0$.

If we write $\beta_1{}^2 = \alpha_{11}$, $\beta_2{}^2 = \alpha_{22}$ where $\beta_1 = 1 + jB_1(rs)$, $\beta_2 = 1 + jB_2(rs)$, the function

$$\xi_m = \frac{e^{\frac{m\pi(d-y)}{c}\beta} - e^{\frac{-m\pi(d-y)}{c}\beta}}{e^{\frac{m\pi d}{c}\beta} - e^{\frac{-m\pi d}{c}\beta}} \cdot \sin \frac{m\pi x}{c},$$

in which

$$\beta = \frac{1}{\beta_2}\beta_1 = 1 + jB(rs),$$

will be a particular solution of (59') which vanishes for $x = 0$, $x = c$, $y = d$ and takes on the value $\sin m\pi x/c$ for $y = 0$. The function

$$\xi = \sum_1^\infty{}_m \xi_m \widetilde{\omega}_m,$$

with

$$\widetilde{\omega}_m = \frac{2}{c} \int_0^c \xi_{y=0} \sin \frac{m\pi x}{c} dx,$$

will be the solution which takes on given values for $y = 0$, assuming the necessary conditions for convergence. Our problem is solved if we let

$$\xi_{y=0} = jf(x, r, s).$$

* The special case in which I describe this function as reducing to the ordinary Green's function is invalid (*Rendiconti del Circolo Matematico di Palermo*, vol. 34, p. 25).

† Volterra, *Rendiconti della R. Accademia dei Lincei*, vol. 21, 2d semester, p. 1; Evans, ibid., p. 25.

In case the length d is allowed to become infinite, the solution takes the form

$$
(60) \qquad U(xy \mid rs) = \sum_{1}^{\infty} {}_{m} e^{\frac{-m\pi y}{c}} \left\{ P_m(rs) \right.
$$
$$
\left. + \int_a^b E\left(0, \frac{-m\pi y}{c} B(rt) \right) P_m(ts) dt \right\} \sin \frac{m\pi x}{c},
$$

with

$$
P_m(rs) = \frac{2}{c} \int_0^c f(xrs) \sin \frac{m\pi x}{c} dx.
$$

Instead of constant limits ab in (59″) and (60) we may of course use variable limits sr. It is noticeable that the variable s takes merely the role of a parameter in both (59″) and (60), and so the solution may be regarded merely as a function of the three variables x, y, r, the s being omitted.

79. The Cauchy Problem for Integro-Differential Equations. Consider the system of partial equations

$$
(61) \qquad \frac{\partial \xi_i}{\partial y} = F_i\left(\frac{\partial \xi_1}{\partial x}, \cdots, \frac{\partial \xi_n}{\partial x}; \xi_1, \cdots, \xi_n; x, y \mid rs \right),
$$

where the F_i are analytic functions of their first $2n + 2$ arguments, in a certain $(2n + 2)$-dimensional neighborhood, with coefficients which are continuous functions of r and s $(a \leqq r \leqq b, a \leqq s \leqq b)$. The $(2n + 2)$-dimensional neighborhood is to include the values determined by the ordinary coefficients of certain given functions $\xi_1^0(x \mid rs), \cdots, \xi_n^0(x \mid rs)$, which are analytic in x in the neighborhood of $x = 0$. These functions are assumed to contain a parameter λ in accordance with (35).

THEOREM. *There is one and only one system of solutions $\xi_1, \cdots, \xi_n$ of (61) which are analytic at the origin in x and y, and which, for $y = 0$, take on the given values $\xi_1^0, \cdots, \xi_n^0$.*

The proof of this theorem is based on the convergence theorem already given. It serves as a generalization of some of Volterra's theorems which establish the existence of what corresponds to general and complete integrals of integro-differential equations of this type. The unique determination of these solutions by initial conditions depends however on the theory of division developed in terms of the complex algebra.

If the coefficients (as functions of r, s) of the F_i are permutable among themselves and with the functions $\xi_1^0, \cdots, \xi_n^0$, the solutions will be permutable with those coefficients and with each other.

Any integro-differential equation of static type, if it can be solved for the highest derivative with respect to y, can be rewritten in the form (61). In particular, the equation described in (59), (59′), or (59″) may be reduced to that form unless $A_{22}(rs)$ fails to have a resolvent kernel. Hence if $D_{A_{22}} \neq 0$, (59″) has a unique analytic solution which with its first derivative in regard to y is arbitrarily assigned (analytically in x) on the x-axis.

In general, to reduce an integro-differential equation to symbolic form involves substituting the quantity $\xi = jU$ for the unknown $U(xy \mid rs)$. In the symbolic form, we are interested, therefore, mainly in solutions of nullity.

This remark has bearing in connection with the theory of *characteristics*. Consider the equation of the second order, linear in the derivatives of highest order:

$$(62) \qquad \alpha_{11} \frac{\partial^2 \xi}{\partial x^2} + 2\alpha_{12} \frac{\partial^2 \xi}{\partial x \partial y} + \alpha_{22} \frac{\partial^2 \xi}{\partial y^2} + \lambda = 0,$$

the quantities α_{11}, α_{12}, α_{22}, λ being functions of ξ, $\partial\xi/\partial x$, $\partial\xi/\partial y$, x, y, r, s of the type previously specified, with the region of analyticity as the neighborhood of the analytic curve $y = \varphi(x)$. We assume that along this curve we are given ξ and $\partial\xi/\partial y$, or what amounts to the same thing, ξ, $\partial\xi/\partial x$, $\partial\xi/\partial y$ as analytic functions of x.

Precisely as in the theory of differential equations,[*] by expressing $\partial^2\xi/\partial x^2$ and $\partial^2\xi/\partial x\,\partial y$ for points on $y = \varphi(x)$ in terms of $\partial\xi \mid \partial y$ and $\partial^2\xi/\partial y^2$, we have from (62), as the equation for the determination of $\partial^2\xi/\partial y^2$, the following:

$$(63) \qquad \Gamma\xi_{22} + \Pi = 0,$$

in which

$$(64) \qquad \begin{aligned} \Gamma &= \alpha_{11}\left(\frac{dy}{dx}\right)^2 - 2\alpha_{12}\frac{dy}{dx} + \alpha_{22}, \\ \Pi &= \alpha_{11}\left(\frac{d\xi_1}{dx} - \frac{dy}{dx}\frac{d\xi_2}{dx}\right) + 2\alpha_{12}\frac{d\xi_2}{dx} + \lambda, \end{aligned}$$

where d/dx refers to differentiation along the curve, and ξ_1 and ξ_2 denote $\partial\xi/\partial x$ and $\partial\xi/\partial y$ respectively. In these equations it is important to preserve the order of all quantities that involve the j, so as not to necessitate the introduction of a hypothesis of permutability.

The equation (63) enables us to determine ξ_{22} unless $\Gamma = g + jG$ is a function of nullity at some point of the curve $y = \varphi(x)$; i. e., unless

$$(65) \qquad g = 0.$$

The curves defined by (65) may be called the *ordinary characteristics* of the integro-differential equation. On account of the way the symbolic equation is formed from the integro-differential equation, equation (65), which involves no functional coefficients, is a pure differential equation, and is independent of the solution $\xi = jU$. *The ordinary characteristics are independent of the solution of the integro-differential equation, and depend merely on its coefficients.*

If we make an analytic transformation of the independent variables x, y which reduces the curve $y = \varphi(x)$ to the x-axis, it is immediately verifiable that a sufficient condition that the transformed equation be solvable for $\partial^2\xi/\partial y^2$ is that the curve $y = \varphi(x)$ be nowhere tangent to an ordinary characteristic. *If $y = \varphi(x)$ is nowhere tangent to an ordinary characteristic, the given values of U and $\partial U/\partial y$ uniquely determine a solution of the integro-differential equation.*

On the other hand, this condition is not necessary, since it is sometimes possible to divide by a function of nullity. It may happen that every curve in the plane is an ordinary characteristic, and yet that given values of U and

---

[*] Hadamard, Leçons sur la propogation des ondes, Paris (1913), chap. 7.

$\partial U/\partial y$ uniquely determine a solution in the neighborhood of $y = \varphi(x)$. For the equation, by differentiation or perhaps in other ways, may be transformed into one with definite ordinary characteristics to which $y = \varphi(x)$ is nowhere tangent.

If, however, along an ordinary characteristic we are able to determine ξ so that the functional coefficient of Γ shall vanish:

$$(66) \qquad\qquad G = 0,$$

the solution and its derivatives will be defined all along the characteristic, provided they are defined at a single point of it.

80. Functions of Nullity. In general, as in the preceding paragraphs, the region between necessary and sufficient conditions is filled by the theory of functions of nullity. The difficulty of this theory is commensurate with that of the integral equation of the first kind, on which it is based.

Volterra has given a comprehensive treatment of this subject, for the combination of the first kind, of wider import than its sub-title in these lectures suggests. Consider then, without regard to the complex units, the combination

$$(67) \qquad \psi = \overset{*}{g}\overset{*}{\varphi} = \int_s^r g(rs_1)\varphi(s_1 s)ds_1,$$

according to the notation of Volterra. The mth power of f is thus obviously defined.

If m is such that

$$(68) \qquad\qquad \psi(rs) = (r - s)^m f(rs),$$

with $f(rs)$ continuous and $f(ss) \neq 0$, ψ is said to be a *function of order $m + 1$*. In (68), $f(rs)$ is called the *characteristic* of $\psi(rs)$, and $f(rr)$ is called its *diagonal*.

The product in the above sense of a function of order m and a function of order n is of order $m + n$, and the mth power of a function of order n is of order mn.

The solution of the equation

$$\overset{*}{\psi}\overset{*}{\psi} = f$$

allows us to define $\overset{*}{f}{}^{1/2}$. In fact if f is of order 1, $\overset{*}{f}{}^{1/2}$ is of order $\frac{1}{2}$,

i. e., becomes infinite to the order $\frac{1}{2}$ as r approaches s.   Similarly $\overset{*}{f}{}^{1/n}$ may be defined, and turns out to be of order $1/n$, i. e., to become infinite like $(s - r)^{n-1/n}$.   There will be n quantities $\overset{*}{f}{}^{1/n}$, obtained by multiplying one of them by the nth roots of unity.

These functions, $\overset{*}{f}{}^{m}, \overset{*}{f}{}^{1/n}$, and also $\overset{*}{f}{}^{m/n} = (\overset{*}{f}{}^{1/n})^{m}$, turn out to be permutable with f itself.   Since two functions permutable with a third are permutable with each other, the functions permutable with a given function form what may be called a group of *permutable functions*.   *Given a function of order 1 we have therefore seen how to find a function of any assigned rational order which belongs to its group.*

If f is a function of a certain order α, whose diagonal is positive, then we have

$$\overset{*}{f}{}^{m/n} = (r - s)^{m\alpha/n-1}L\left(rs\,\bigg|\,\frac{m}{n}\right),$$

where the function L is the characteristic, taken with a positive diagonal.   Suppose that as m/n approaches z, $L(rs\,|\,m/n)$ approaches some function $L(rs\,|\,z)$ uniformly;   then if z is irrational, we define

$$\overset{*}{f}{}^{z} = \lim_{m/n=z} \overset{*}{f}{}^{m/n}.$$

On this basis it can be shown that all the algebraic calculus of positive exponents becomes extensible to the theory of powers of composition, and we have

(69)
$$\overset{*}{f}{}^{z}\overset{*}{f}{}^{z_1} = \overset{*}{f}{}^{z+z_1},$$
$$(\overset{*}{f}{}^{z})^{z_1} = \overset{*}{f}{}^{zz_1},$$

Further elements $\overset{*}{f}/\overset{*}{\psi}, \overset{*}{f}{}^{-1}, \overset{*}{f}_0$ can be defined so as to be included in a group of permutable functions;   they no longer all denote functions in the ordinary sense, but serve as abstract elements which may be used in calculation according to the commutative, distributive and associative laws, and serve to lead from functions which have a real meaning in the ordinary sense to others which have also a real meaning by means of these formal processes.

Thus the function

$$F[f] = \overset{*}{f}{}^0 + f + \frac{1}{2!}\overset{*}{f}{}^2 + \frac{1}{3!}\overset{*}{f}{}^3 + \cdots$$

may be defined; for which, as in Art. 76, there is the formal addition theorem

$$F[\overset{*}{f} + \overset{*}{\varphi}] = F[\overset{*}{f}]F[\overset{*}{\varphi}],$$

f and φ being two functions of the same group, and the periodicity property

$$F[\overset{*}{f} + 2\pi i f_0] = F[\overset{*}{f}],$$

formal properties which however become actual upon combination with other functions of the same group.

Given a function φ of definite positive order, we have the series

$$\cdots \overset{*}{\varphi}{}^{-3}, \overset{*}{\varphi}{}^{-2}, \overset{*}{\varphi}{}^{-1}, \overset{*}{\varphi}{}^{0}, \varphi, \overset{*}{\varphi}{}^{2}, \overset{*}{\varphi}{}^{3}, \cdots$$

which may be called a *progression of composition*, with *ratio* or *base* φ. The exponents are called the *logarithms of composition*. The study of these logarithms leads to a new category of integral equations and to the solution of these equations.

APPENDIX

POINCARÉ THEORY OF INTEGRALS OF FUNCTIONS OF TWO COMPLEX VARIABLES

1. Poincaré's theory of functions of two complex variables in their relation to integrals over two dimensional surface caps, of given boundaries, and the generalization of the notion of residue, were based on the procedure of enveloping such a surface in three-dimensional spaces. It was discussed only briefly in Lecture II. Here it is proposed to describe Poincaré's ideas in somewhat more detail and exhibit, in the simplest possible case, the relation between the methods of Poincaré and Volterra.*

Following Poincaré, let us write

$$F(\xi,\eta) = F_1(x,y,z,t) + iF_2(x,y,z,t)$$
$$\xi = x + iy, \quad \eta = z + it,$$

and assume that, for the variables ξ and η separately, the Cauchy–Riemann (C–R) equations are satisfied:

$$(1) \quad \frac{\partial F_1}{\partial x} = \frac{\partial F_2}{\partial y}, \quad \frac{\partial F_2}{\partial x} = -\frac{\partial F_1}{\partial y}, \quad \frac{\partial F_1}{\partial z} = \frac{\partial F_2}{\partial t}, \quad \frac{\partial F_2}{\partial z} = -\frac{\partial F_1}{\partial t}.$$

The surface of integration σ of (48), Lecture II, with boundary

---

*The relevant publications are the following:

Poincaré, *Comptes Rendus de l'Académie des Sciences*, Paris, v. 102 (1886), p. 102; *Acta Mathematica*, v. 9 (1887), pp. 233–286 (citation of page 30, Lecture II).

Volterra, Notes in the *Acc. dei Lincei, Rendiconti*, as follows: for the three dimensional case, v. III_2 (1887), pp. 281–287; v. IV_1 (1888), pp. 107–115 and 196–202 (reference to Poincaré, p. 202); expounded in the *Acta* memoir (citation of page 30, Lecture II); and for r-spaces in n-space, v. V_1 (1889), pp. 158–165, 291–299, and 599–611, and exposition in English (citation of page 30, Lecture II). The English exposition does not include the subject of the last note in the *Rendiconti*, which begins with the representation of electric currents and magnetic fields as *conjugate* functions and deals with the corresponding generalization to hyperspaces.

C, is enclosed in a three-dimensional neighborhood by introducing parameters λ, μ, ν, writing

(2) $x = \varphi_1$, $y = \varphi_2$, $z = \varphi_3$, $t = \varphi_4$ where $\varphi_j = \varphi_j(\lambda\mu\nu)$.

By taking $\lambda = u$, $\mu = v$, where u and v are curvilinear coordinates on the surface of integration σ, Poincaré defines the integral by the formula

(3)
$$J = \iint_\sigma \left\{ (F_1 + iF_2) \frac{\partial(x,z)}{\partial(u,v)} + (iF_1 - F_2) \frac{\partial(x,t)}{\partial(u,v)} \right.$$
$$\left. + (iF_1 - F_2) \frac{\partial(y,z)}{\partial(u,v)} - (F_1 + iF_2) \frac{\partial(y,t)}{\partial(u,v)} \right\} dudv,$$

thus being independent of the choice of such coordinates, subject to the condition that the new coordinates denote a point on the boundary C when and only when u, v do so. He considers in fact the more general problem of two-dimensional surfaces in n-space.

In 4-space, as a special case, the situation reduces to the consideration of functions $X_i(x_1,x_2,x_3,x_4)$. Poincaré employs the notion (X_i,X_j) to denote again certain given functions such that (X_j,X_i) is the function $- (X_i,X_j)$.* He considers the integral

$$J = \iint_\sigma \sum (X_i,X_j)dx_idx_j, \quad i,j = 1, 2, 3, 4,$$

the $\sum$ denoting the sum over independent (X_i,X_j). The significance of the minus sign above is the retention of the relation

$$(X_i,X_j) \frac{\partial(x_i,x_j)}{\partial(u,v)} = (X_j,X_i) \frac{\partial(x_j,x_i)}{\partial(u,v)}.$$

In particular $(X_i,X_i) = 0$. Accordingly there are six independent (X_i,X_j).

Let ν be a third independent variable w subject to the restriction that w is constant on C. The problem then is to find necessary and sufficient conditions that $\partial J/\partial w = 0$. By means

*As far as the present exposition is concerned it might equally well be written $(X_i,X_j) = X_{ij} = -X_{ji}$.

of a classical method of the Calculus of Variations, Poincaré obtains the formula

$$\frac{dJ}{dw} = \iint\limits_{\sigma} \sum \left\{ \frac{\partial(X_i, X_j)}{\partial x_k} + \frac{\partial(X_j, X_k)}{\partial x_i} + \frac{\partial(X_k, X_i)}{\partial x_j} \right\} \frac{d(x_i, x_j, x_k)}{d(u, v, w)} \, du dv.$$

Since the expression in brackets is a given point function, $dJ/dw = 0$ implies that that expression must vanish. Hence

$$(4) \qquad \frac{\partial(X_i, X_j)}{\partial x_k} + \frac{\partial(X_j, X_k)}{\partial x_i} + \frac{\partial(X_k, X_i)}{\partial x_j} = 0.$$

In the case of the integral (3), we have

$$J = \iint\limits_{\sigma} \{ (X, Y)dxdy + (X, Z)dxdz + (X, T)dxdt + (Y, Z)dydz$$

$$+ (Y, T)dydt + (Z, T)dzdt \},$$

where $(X, Y) = 0$, $(Z, T) = 0$, and

$$(X, Z) = F_1 + iF_2, \quad (Y, T) = -(F_1 + iF_2) = -(T, Y)$$
$$(X, T) = (Y, Z) = iF_1 - F_2.$$

Calculation of (4) yields immediately the C–R equations (1).

If σ_1 and σ_2 are two (orientable) surfaces in the (λ, μ, ν) space, with common boundary C, it follows that the conditions (1) imply that $J(\sigma_1) = J(\sigma_2)$, provided that $F(\xi, \eta)$ has no singularity in the enclosed regions, and therefore that $J(\sigma)$ is a functional of C. Thus in Lecture II we obtained the relations (50) and (51).

If S is a closed surface in a (λ, μ, ν)-space and S' is a closed surface in the interior domain $T(S)$ of S, the conditions (1), holding everywhere in the domain bounded by S and S', insure that $J(S') = J(S)$. Accordingly, if there is a closed set C_0 of singularities of $F(\xi, \eta)$, and an S' such that $C_0 \subset T(S') \subset T(S)$, we may regard the $J(S')$ as taking the place of a curvilinear integral in the plane of a single complex variable for the purpose of calculating residues.

2. As a first application of the notion of residue, Poincaré examines in detail the function

$$(5) \qquad F(\xi,\eta) = \frac{P(\xi,\eta)}{Q(\xi,\eta)R(\xi,\eta)} = \frac{P_1 + iP_2}{(Q_1 + iQ_2)(R_1 + iR_2)}$$

$P(\xi, \eta)$ being uniform and analytic in $T(S)$, and $Q(\xi, \eta)$ and $R(\xi, N)$ irreducible polynomials. The equation $Q(\xi, \eta) = 0$,

$$(6) \qquad Q_1(x,y,z,t) = 0 = Q_2(x,y,z,t)$$

determines closed surfaces in the 4-space. It is assumed that the $\varphi_i(\lambda,\mu,\nu)$ are chosen so that the (λ,μ,ν)-space is in *general position* with respect to (6)—that is, so that the surface (6) and the (λ,μ,ν)-space intersect in a curve—and that S in the three-space can be chosen so that $T(S)$ contains just one closed curve C_0 of $Q = 0$ and no points of $R = 0$.

If C_0 contains no double points, the region $T(S')$, $C_0 \subset T(S')$ $\subset T(S)$, can be shrunk down to a toroidal neighborhood of C_0. By means then of a suitable choice of toroidal coordinates the integral J can be reduced to an iterated integral over C_0 itself, say first with respect to η and second ξ. The first integration, for fixed ξ, gives a residue in the usual sense, and the second yields the formula

$$J = 2\pi i \int_{C_0} \frac{P d\xi}{R \partial Q / \partial \eta}$$

with of course an analogous integral J' for a curve of $R = 0$, and both are evaluated as *periods* of the integrals.

Consider small changes of the functions φ_i, $i = 1,\ldots, 4$. If S is unchanged, the integral over S is unchanged although C_0 may be displaced in the two-dimensional surface (6), and if C_0 is unchanged but S displaced (in 4-space) the integral over C_0 is invariant. Accordingly as both S and C_0 change, the value of J is unchanged until the hypothesis on C_0 is no longer valid—that is, until C_0 attains a double point or intersects a curve of $R = 0$. Poincaré obtains the resulting periods in detail: as *cyclic*, depending mainly on the genus of $Q = 0$ and that of $R = 0$, and *polar*, depending on the double points of $Q = 0$ and

$R = 0$ and the points of intersection of the two, as long as they are not confounded with the zeros of $P = 0$.

"Il n'est pas douteux qu'on ne puisse tirer des principes qui précèdent une foule d'applications différents"—of which Poincaré discusses several interesting cases. But of course all this is of long ago, and the subject of several complex variables has expanded greatly in several directions.*

3. We proceed to the comparison of functions of one complex variable, $F(z) = F_1(x,y) + iF_2(x,y)$, and their integrals, with complex functionals that are based on complex vectors $V_1 + iV_2$, V_1 and V_2 being vector functions of points in the x, y plane.

Let T be a bounded domain in the x, y plane, of which the boundaries are simple closed curves finite in number, and let s, s', s'' be coterminal simple arcs with initial point M_1 and terminal point M_2, such that $s' - s''$ is the counterclockwise boundary of a single domain $T(s',s'')$ contained in T, and that the arcs have sufficient smoothness for the operations to be carried out. We assume that the functions, defined below, have the sufficient smoothness for operations on them—for example, that the vectors V and W below be continuously differentiable in T.

4. Let $V = V_1 + iV_2$ be a complex valued vector in the plane, in terms of real components:

$V_1 = (V_{1x}, V_{1y})$, $V_2 = (V_{2x}, V_{2y})$, functions of x, y, and by K_s denote the integral

$$
(7) \quad
\begin{aligned}
K_s &= \int_s V_n ds \\
&= \int_s \{(V_{1x} + iV_{2x}) \cos x,n + (V_{1y} + iV_{2y}) \cos y,n\} ds,
\end{aligned}
$$

*Cf. for instance, S. Bochner and W. T. Martin, Several complex variables (1948), 216 pp., *Princeton Mathematical Series*, Princeton, New Jersey; W. V. D. Hodge, Theory and applications of harmonic integrals (1952), 282 pp., Cambridge, England.

where, for definiteness, n is the direction of the normal so that $\sphericalangle s,n = -\pi/2$, n thus being the exterior normal for $s'-s''$. Since $\cos x,n = \cos y,s$, $\cos y,n = -\cos x,s$, we may write

$$(8) \quad K_s = \int_s \{(V_{1x} + iV_{2x}) \cos y,s - (V_{1y} + iV_{2y}) \cos x,s\}ds.$$

Thus the vector V corresponds to the flux vector in 3-space.

For all s',s'' as above, we have $K_{s'} = K_{s''}$ if and only if Div $V = 0$ in T, that is, if

$$(9) \quad \frac{\partial V_{1x}}{\partial x} + \frac{\partial V_{1y}}{\partial y} = 0, \quad \frac{\partial V_{2x}}{\partial x} + \frac{\partial V_{2y}}{\partial y} = 0, \quad (x,y) \text{ in } T.$$

In this case, K_s is an additive functional of the end points of s, $K[M_1,M_2] = K_s$, taking account of possible "periods." We restrict ourselves to such functionals.

Denote by W a second vector of the same sort as V, with Div $W = 0$, and by $L[M_1,M_2] = L_s$, the additive functional based on W. In order for L and K to be isogenous it is necessary and sufficient that $W = \varphi V$, $\varphi = \varphi_1(x,y) + i\varphi_2(x,y)$, $V = \psi W$, with $\varphi = \varphi_1(x,y) + i\varphi_2(x,y)$, not necessarily analytic in $z = x + iy$, and $\psi = 1/\varphi$, both φ and ψ bounded in T.*

4.1. With regard to the vectors of § 4, a special interest belongs to the case:

$$(10) \quad V_{1x} = V_{2y}, \quad V_{1y} = -V_{2x}.$$

The following propositions are easily verified:

(a) If (10), and if φ is a point function $\varphi_1(x,y) + i\varphi_2(x,y)$ in T, and $W = \varphi V$, then

$$(10') \quad W_{1x} = W_{2y}, \quad W_{1y} = -W_{2x}.$$

(b) If K and L are additive and isogenous and if (10), then φ is analytic in T except where $V = 0$. If, further, the zeros of V are isolated, φ is analytic in T and $\neq 0$

(c) If K and L are additive and isogenous, and φ is analytic in T, then (10) and (10') are valid in T.

---

* Since $\varphi_1 + i\varphi_2$ is scalar,
$W_{1x} = R(\varphi_1 + i\varphi_2)(V_{1x}+iV_{2x})$, $W_{2x} = Im(\varphi_1 + i\varphi_2)(V_{1x} + iV_{2x})$, etc.

(d) With the hypotheses of (c), K_s and L_s may be reduced to the forms

$$K_8 = K(z) = -\int_{(M_1)}^{z} (V_{1y} + iV_{1x})dz,$$

$$L_s = L(z) = -\int_{(M_1)}^{z} (W_{1y} + iW_{1x})dz.$$

The integrands are analytic in T; the integrals $K(z)$ and $L(z)$ are also, except for possible "periods."

The statement (a) is verified by carrying out the multiplication of the vector $V = (V_{1x} - iV_{1y}, V_{1y} + iV_{1x})$ by the scalar $\varphi_1 + i\varphi_2$.

If K is additive, $K[M_1,M]$, with M_1 fixed, is merely a function of the terminal point M of s, to be written as $K(z)$. Similarly L will be $L(z)$. We have the homogeneous equations

(11)
$$V_{1x}\frac{\partial\varphi_1}{\partial x} + V_{1y}\frac{\partial\varphi_1}{\partial y} - V_{2x}\frac{\partial\varphi_2}{\partial x} - V_{2y}\frac{\partial\varphi_2}{\partial y} = 0$$

$$V_{1x}\frac{\partial\varphi_2}{\partial x} + V_{1y}\frac{\partial\varphi_2}{\partial y} + V_{2x}\frac{\partial\varphi_1}{\partial x} + V_{2y}\frac{\partial\varphi_1}{\partial y} = 0.$$

In fact, from Div $V = 0$, Div $W = 0$, there follows the equation $(V_1 + iV_2)\cdot(\nabla\varphi_1 + \nabla\varphi_2) = 0$ for the scalar product $V\cdot\varphi$.

For (b) substitute $V_{2x} = -V_{1y}$, $V_{2y} = V_{1x}$ in (11), and for (c) substitute from the C–R equations $\partial\varphi_2/\partial x = -\partial\varphi_1/\partial y$, $\partial\varphi_2/\partial y = \partial\varphi_1/\partial x$. The desired results follow from the values of the determinants in the resulting pairs of equations. The second part of (b) is a consequence of the boundedness of φ. As for (c), the determinant D,

$$D = \pm\{(V_{1x} - V_{2y})^2 + (V_{1y} + V_{2x})^2\},$$

must vanish except when $\partial\varphi_1/\partial x$ and $\partial\varphi_1/\partial y$ both vanish. But the zeros of $d\varphi/dz$ are isolated in T and V is continuous; therefore (c).

Finally (d). Substitution in (8) of $\cos x,s\,ds = dx$, $\cos y,s$

$ds = dy$ yields $K(z)$; $L(z)$ is similar. Substitution of (10) in (9) and an analogous use of (10') yield the additional relations

$$(12) \qquad \frac{\partial V_{1y}}{\partial x} - \frac{\partial V_{1x}}{\partial y} = 0, \qquad \frac{\partial W_{1y}}{\partial x} - \frac{\partial W_{1x}}{\partial y} = 0.$$

But from (9), with the corresponding Div $W = 0$, and (12) follow the C–R equations: for example, in the case of $K(z)$,

$$\left(\frac{\partial}{\partial x} + i\, \frac{\partial}{\partial y} \right) (V_{1y} + iV_{1x})$$

$$= \left(\frac{\partial V_{1y}}{\partial x} - \frac{\partial V_{1x}}{\partial y} \right) + i \left(\frac{\partial V_{1y}}{\partial y} + \frac{\partial V_{1x}}{\partial x} \right) = 0.$$

The final clause of (d) is a basic property of the integral.

4.2. Let $F(z) = F_1(x,y) + iF_2(x,y)$ be analytic in T, and $G(z) = G_1 + iG_2$ similarly. Define

$$I(z) = \int_{z_1}^{z} (F_1 + iF_2)(dx + idy),$$

$$J(z) = \int_{z_1}^{z} (G_1 + iG_2)(dx + idy)$$

and let $I(z)$ and $J(z)$ be isogenous. Then there exists $f(z)$ such that $G(z)/F(z) = f(z)$ where $f(z)$ and $1/f(z)$ are bounded, therefore analytic, in T.

In order for K to be equal to I a comparison of (8) with the above yields the relations

$$V_{2x} = -V_{1y} = -F_1, \quad V_{2y} = V_{1x} = -F_2,$$

because the direction of ds is arbitrary. The C–R relations for F are equivalent to (9) and (12). Accordingly if $\varphi(z)$ is taken as $f(z)$, $L(z)$ will be equal to $J(z)$.

The complex function theory in the plane is a particular case of the additive functional theory, for the determination of which the conditions (10) are essentially necessary and sufficient. Volterra's treatment as given in the cited *Acta Mathematica* memoir, is a theory of complex functions of curves in a given 3-space, whereas Poincaré, as we have seen, makes use of a variable 3-space, which encloses a two-dimensional surface in the given 4-space of ξ, η. Therefore the two treatments, aside from certain formal connections, have different ranges of interest. It would be the last three notes of Volterra, cited in this Appendix, dealing with functionals of r-spaces in an n-space, taking $r = 1$, $n = 4$, that would include as a special case the functions of two complex variables.

INDEX OF AUTHORS

CATALOGUE OF DOVER BOOKS

BOOKS EXPLAINING SCIENCE AND MATHEMATICS

General

WHAT IS SCIENCE?, Norman Campbell. This excellent introduction explains scientific method, role of mathematics, types of scientific laws. Contents: 2 aspects of science, science & nature, laws of science, discovery of laws, explanation of laws, measurement & numerical laws, applications of science. 192pp. 5⅜ x 8. S43 Paperbound **$1.25**

THE COMMON SENSE OF THE EXACT SCIENCES, W. K. Clifford. Introduction by James Newman, edited by Karl Pearson. For 70 years this has been a guide to classical scientific and mathematical thought. Explains with unusual clarity basic concepts, such as extension of meaning of symbols, characteristics of surface boundaries, properties of plane figures, vectors, Cartesian method of determining position, etc. Long preface by Bertrand Russell. Bibliography of Clifford. Corrected, 130 diagrams redrawn. 249pp. 5⅜ x 8. T61 Paperbound **$1.60**

SCIENCE THEORY AND MAN, Erwin Schrödinger. This is a complete and unabridged reissue of SCIENCE AND THE HUMAN TEMPERAMENT plus an additional essay: "What is an Elementary Particle?" Nobel laureate Schrödinger discusses such topics as nature of scientific method, the nature of science, chance and determinism, science and society, conceptual models for physical entities, elementary particles and wave mechanics. Presentation is popular and may be followed by most people with little or no scientific training. "Fine practical preparation for a time when laws of nature, human institutions . . . are undergoing a critical examination without parallel," Waldemar Kaempffert, N. Y. TIMES. 192pp. 5⅜ x 8. T428 Paperbound **$1.35**

FADS AND FALLACIES IN THE NAME OF SCIENCE, Martin Gardner. Examines various cults, quack systems, frauds, delusions which at various times have masqueraded as science. Accounts of hollow-earth fanatics like Symmes; Velikovsky and wandering planets; Hoerbiger; Bellamy and the theory of multiple moons; Charles Fort; dowsing, pseudoscientific methods for finding water, ores, oil. Sections on naturopathy, iridiagnosis, zone therapy, food fads, etc. Analytical accounts of Wilhelm Reich and orgone sex energy; L. Ron Hubbard and Dianetics; A. Korzybski and General Semantics; many others. Brought up to date to include Bridey Murphy, others. Not just a collection of anecdotes, but a fair, reasoned appraisal of eccentric theory. Formerly titled IN THE NAME OF SCIENCE. Preface. Index. x + 384pp. 5⅜ x 8. T394 Paperbound **$1.50**

A DOVER SCIENCE SAMPLER, edited by George Barkin. 64-page book, sturdily bound, containing excerpts from over 20 Dover books, explaining science. Edwin Hubble, George Sarton, Ernst Mach, A. d'Abro, Galileo, Newton, others, discussing island universes, scientific truth, biological phenomena, stability in bridges, etc. Copies limited; no more than 1 to a customer, FREE

POPULAR SCIENTIFIC LECTURES, Hermann von Helmholtz. Helmholtz was a superb expositor as well as a scientist of genius in many areas. The seven essays in this volume are models of clarity, and even today they rank among the best general descriptions of their subjects ever written. "The Physiological Causes of Harmony in Music" was the first significant physiological explanation of musical consonance and dissonance. Two essays, "On the Interaction of Natural Forces" and "On the Conservation of Force," were of great importance in the history of science, for they firmly established the principle of the conservation of energy. Other lectures include "On the Relation of Optics to Painting," "On Recent Progress in the Theory of Vision," "On Goethe's Scientific Researches," and "On the Origin and Significance of Geometrical Axioms." Selected and edited with an introduction by Professor Morris Kline. xii + 286pp. 5⅜ x 8½. T799 Paperbound **$1.45**

BOOKS EXPLAINING SCIENCE AND MATHEMATICS

Physics

CONCERNING THE NATURE OF THINGS, Sir William Bragg. Christmas lectures delivered at the Royal Society by Nobel laureate. Why a spinning ball travels in a curved track; how uranium is transmuted to lead, etc. Partial contents: atoms, gases, liquids, crystals, metals, etc. No scientific background needed; wonderful for intelligent child. 32pp. of photos, 57 figures. xii + 232pp. 5⅜ x 8. T31 Paperbound **$1.35**

THE RESTLESS UNIVERSE, Max Born. New enlarged version of this remarkably readable account by a Nobel laureate. Moving from sub-atomic particles to universe, the author explains in very simple terms the latest theories of wave mechanics. Partial contents: air and its relatives, electrons & ions, waves & particles, electronic structure of the atom, nuclear physics. Nearly 1000 illustrations, including 7 animated sequences. 325pp. 6 x 9. T412 Paperbound **$2.00**

FROM EUCLID TO EDDINGTON: A STUDY OF THE CONCEPTIONS OF THE EXTERNAL WORLD, Sir Edmund Whittaker. A foremost British scientist traces the development of theories of natural philosophy from the western rediscovery of Euclid to Eddington, Einstein, Dirac, etc. The inadequacy of classical physics is contrasted with present day attempts to understand the physical world through relativity, non-Euclidean geometry, space curvature, wave mechanics, etc. 5 major divisions of examination: Space; Time and Movement; the Concepts of Classical Physics; the Concepts of Quantum Mechanics; the Eddington Universe. 212pp. 5⅜ x 8.
T491 Paperbound **$1.35**

PHYSICS, THE PIONEER SCIENCE, L. W. Taylor. First thorough text to place all important physical phenomena in cultural-historical framework; remains best work of its kind. Exposition of physical laws, theories developed chronologically, with great historical, illustrative experiments diagrammed, described, worked out mathematically. Excellent physics text for self-study as well as class work. Vol. 1: Heat, Sound: motion, acceleration, gravitation, conservation of energy, heat engines, rotation, heat, mechanical energy, etc. 211 illus. 407pp. 5⅜ x 8. Vol. 2: Light, Electricity: images, lenses, prisms, magnetism, Ohm's law, dynamos, telegraph, quantum theory, decline of mechanical view of nature, etc. Bibliography. 13 table appendix. Index. 551 illus. 2 color plates. 508pp. 5⅜ x 8.

Vol. 1 S565 Paperbound **$2.00**
Vol. 2 S566 Paperbound **$2.00**
The set **$4.00**

A SURVEY OF PHYSICAL THEORY, Max Planck. One of the greatest scientists of all time, creator of the quantum revolution in physics, writes in non-technical terms of his own discoveries and those of other outstanding creators of modern physics. Planck wrote this book when science had just crossed the threshold of the new physics, and he communicates the excitement felt then as he discusses electromagnetic theories, statistical methods, evolution of the concept of light, a step-by-step description of how he developed his own momentous theory, and many more of the basic ideas behind modern physics. Formerly "A Survey of Physics." Bibliography. Index. 128pp. 5⅜ x 8.
S650 Paperbound **$1.15**

THE ATOMIC NUCLEUS, M. Korsunsky. The only non-technical comprehensive account of the atomic nucleus in English. For college physics students, etc. Chapters cover: Radioactivity, the Nuclear Model of the Atom, the Mass of Atomic Nuclei, the Disintegration of Atomic Nuclei, the Discovery of the Positron, the Artificial Transformation of Atomic Nuclei, Artificial Radioactivity, Mesons, the Neutrino, the Structure of Atomic Nuclei and Forces Acting Between Nuclear Particles, Nuclear Fission, Chain Reaction, Peaceful Uses, Thermonuclear Reactions. Slightly abridged edition. Translated by G. Yankovsky. 65 figures. Appendix includes 45 photographic illustrations. 413 pp. 5⅜ x 8.
S1052 Paperbound **$2.00**

PRINCIPLES OF MECHANICS SIMPLY EXPLAINED, Morton Mott-Smith. Excellent, highly readable introduction to the theories and discoveries of classical physics. Ideal for the layman who desires a foundation which will enable him to understand and appreciate contemporary developments in the physical sciences. Discusses: Density, The Law of Gravitation, Mass and Weight, Action and Reaction, Kinetic and Potential Energy, The Law of Inertia, Effects of Acceleration, The Independence of Motions, Galileo and the New Science of Dynamics, Newton and the New Cosmos, The Conservation of Momentum, and other topics. Revised edition of "This Mechanical World." Illustrated by E. Kosa, Jr. Bibliography and Chronology. Index. xiv + 171pp. 5⅜ x 8½.
T1067 Paperbound **$1.00**

THE CONCEPT OF ENERGY SIMPLY EXPLAINED, Morton Mott-Smith. Elementary, non-technical exposition which traces the story of man's conquest of energy, with particular emphasis on the developments during the nineteenth century and the first three decades of our own century. Discusses man's earlier efforts to harness energy, more recent experiments and discoveries relating to the steam engine, the engine indicator, the motive power of heat, the principle of excluded perpetual motion, the bases of the conservation of energy, the concept of entropy, the internal combustion engine, mechanical refrigeration, and many other related topics. Also much biographical material. Index. Bibliography. 33 illustrations. ix + 215pp. 5⅜ x 8½.
T1071 Paperbound **$1.25**

HEAT AND ITS WORKINGS, Morton Mott-Smith. One of the best elementary introductions to the theory and attributes of heat, covering such matters as the laws governing the effect of heat on solids, liquids and gases, the methods by which heat is measured, the conversion of a substance from one form to another through heating and cooling, evaporation, the effects of pressure on boiling and freezing points, and the three ways in which heat is transmitted (conduction, convection, radiation). Also brief notes on major experiments and discoveries. Concise, but complete, it presents all the essential facts about the subject in readable style. Will give the layman and beginning student a first-rate background in this major topic in physics. Index. Bibliography. 50 illustrations. x + 165pp. 5⅜ x 8½. T978 Paperbound **$1.00**

THE STORY OF ATOMIC THEORY AND ATOMIC ENERGY, J. G. Feinberg. Wider range of facts on physical theory, cultural implications, than any other similar source. Completely non-technical. Begins with first atomic theory, 600 B.C., goes through A-bomb, developments to 1959. Avogadro, Rutherford, Bohr, Einstein, radioactive decay, binding energy, radiation danger, future benefits of nuclear power, dozens of other topics, told in lively, related, informal manner. Particular stress on European atomic research. "Deserves special mention . . . authoritative," Saturday Review. Formerly "The Atom Story." New chapter to 1959. Index. 34 illustrations. 251pp. 5⅜ x 8.
T625 Paperbound **$1.45**

THE STRANGE STORY OF THE QUANTUM, AN ACCOUNT FOR THE GENERAL READER OF THE GROWTH OF IDEAS UNDERLYING OUR PRESENT ATOMIC KNOWLEDGE, B. Hoffmann. Presents lucidly and expertly, with barest amount of mathematics, the problems and theories which led to modern quantum physics. Dr. Hoffmann begins with the closing years of the 19th century, when certain trifling discrepancies were noticed, and with illuminating analogies and examples takes you through the brilliant concepts of Planck, Einstein, Pauli, de Broglie, Bohr, Schroedinger, Heisenberg, Dirac, Sommerfeld, Feynman, etc. This edition includes a new, long postscript carrying the story through 1958. "Of the books attempting an account of the history and contents of our modern atomic physics which have come to my attention, this is the best," H. Margenau, Yale University, in "American Journal of Physics."; 32 tables and line illustrations. Index. 275pp. 5⅜ x 8.   T518 Paperbound **$1.50**

THE EVOLUTION OF SCIENTIFIC THOUGHT FROM NEWTON TO EINSTEIN, A. d'Abro. Einstein's special and general theories of relativity, with their historical implications, are analyzed in non-technical terms. Excellent accounts of the contributions of Newton, Riemann, Weyl, Planck, Eddington, Maxwell, Lorentz and others are treated in terms of space and time, equations of electromagnetics, finiteness of the universe, methodology of science. 21 diagrams. 482pp. 5⅜ x 8.   T2 Paperound **$2.00**

THE RISE OF THE NEW PHYSICS, A. d'Abro. A half-million word exposition, formerly titled THE DECLINE OF MECHANISM, for readers not versed in higher mathematics. The only thorough explanation, in everyday language, of the central core of modern mathematical physical theory, treating both classical and modern theoretical physics, and presenting in terms almost anyone can understand the equivalent of 5 years of study of mathematical physics. Scientifically impeccable coverage of mathematical-physical thought from the Newtonian system up through the electronic theories of Dirac and Heisenberg and Fermi's statistics. Combines both history and exposition; provides a broad yet unified and detailed view, with constant comparison of classical and modern views on phenomena and theories. "A must for anyone doing serious study in the physical sciences," JOURNAL OF THE FRANKLIN INSTITUTE. "Extraordinary faculty . . . to explain ideas and theories of theoretical physics in the language of daily life," ISIS. First part of set covers philosophy of science, drawing upon the practice of Newton, Maxwell, Poincaré, Einstein, others, discussing modes of thought, experiment, interpretations of causality, etc. In the second part, 100 pages explain grammar and vocabulary of mathematics, with discussions of functions, groups, series, Fourier series, etc. The remainder is devoted to concrete, detailed coverage of both classical and quantum physics, explaining such topics as analytic mechanics, Hamilton's principle, wave theory of light, electromagnetic waves, groups of transformations, thermodynamics, phase rule, Brownian movement, kinetics, special relativity, Planck's original quantum theory, Bohr's atom, Zeeman effect, Broglie's wave mechanics, Heisenberg's uncertainty, Eigen-values, matrices, scores of other important topics. Discoveries and theories are covered for such men as Alembert, Born, Cantor, Debye, Euler, Foucault, Galois, Gauss, Hadamard, Kelvin, Kepler, Laplace, Maxwell, Pauli, Rayleigh, Volterra, Weyl, Young, more than 180 others. Indexed. 97 illustrations. ix + 982pp. 5⅜ x 8.   T3 Volume 1, Paperbound **$2.00**
                                                                 T4 Volume 2, Paperbound **$2.00**

SPINNING TOPS AND GYROSCOPIC MOTION, John Perry. Well-known classic of science still unsurpassed for lucid, accurate, delightful exposition. How quasi-rigidity is induced in flexible and fluid bodies by rapid motions; why gyrostat falls, top rises; nature and effect on climatic conditions of earth's precessional movement; effect of internal fluidity on rotating bodies, etc. Appendixes describe practical uses to which gyroscopes have been put in ships, compasses, monorail transportation. 62 figures. 128pp. 5⅜ x 8.   T416 Paperbound **$1.00**

THE UNIVERSE OF LIGHT, Sir William Bragg. No scientific training needed to read Nobel Prize winner's expansion of his Royal Institute Christmas Lectures. Insight into nature of light, methods and philosophy of science. Explains lenses, reflection, color, resonance, polarization, x-rays, the spectrum, Newton's work with prisms, Huygens' with polarization, Crookes' with cathode ray, etc. Leads into clear statement of 2 major historical theories of light, corpuscle and wave. Dozens of experiments you can do. 199 illus., including 2 full-page color plates. 293pp. 5⅜ x 8.   S538 Paperbound **$1.85**

THE STORY OF X-RAYS FROM RÖNTGEN TO ISOTOPES, A. R. Bleich. Non-technical history of x-rays, their scientific explanation, their applications in medicine, industry, research, and art, and their effect on the individual and his descendants. Includes amusing early reactions to Röntgen's discovery, cancer therapy, detections of art and stamp forgeries, potential risks to patient and operator, etc. Illustrations show x-rays of flower structure, the gall bladder, gears with hidden defects, etc. Original Dover publication. Glossary. Bibliography. Index. 55 photos and figures. xiv + 186pp. 5⅜ x 8.   T662 Paperbound **$1.35**

ELECTRONS, ATOMS, METALS AND ALLOYS, Wm. Hume-Rothery. An introductory-level explanation of the application of the electronic theory to the structure and properties of metals and alloys, taking into account the new theoretical work done by mathematical physicists. Material presented in dialogue-form between an "Old Metallurgist" and a "Young Scientist." Their discussion falls into 4 main parts: the nature of an atom, the nature of a metal, the nature of an alloy, and the structure of the nucleus. They cover such topics as the hydrogen atom, electron waves, wave mechanics, Brillouin zones, co-valent bonds, radio-activity and natural disintegration, fundamental particles, structure and fission of the nucleus, etc. Revised, enlarged edition. 177 illustrations. Subject and name indexes. 407pp. 5⅜ x 8½.   S1046 Paperbound **$2.25**

OUT OF THE SKY, H. H. Nininger. A non-technical but comprehensive introduction to "meteoritics", the young science concerned with all aspects of the arrival of matter from outer space. Written by one of the world's experts on meteorites, this work shows how, despite difficulties of observation and sparseness of data, a considerable body of knowledge has arisen. It defines meteors and meteorites; studies fireball clusters and processions, meteorite composition, size, distribution, showers, explosions, origins, craters, and much more. A true connecting link between astronomy and geology. More than 175 photos, 22 other illustrations. References. Bibliography of author's publications on meteorites. Index. viii + 336pp. 5⅜ x 8. T519 Paperbound **$1.85**

SATELLITES AND SCIENTIFIC RESEARCH, D. King-Hele. Non-technical account of the manmade satellites and the discoveries they have yielded up to the autumn of 1961. Brings together information hitherto published only in hard-to-get scientific journals. Includes the life history of a typical satellite, methods of tracking, new information on the shape of the earth, zones of radiation, etc. Over 60 diagrams and 6 photographs. Mathematical appendix. Bibliography of over 100 items. Index. xii + 180pp. 5⅜ x 8½. T703 Paperbound **$2.00**

BOOKS EXPLAINING SCIENCE AND MATHEMATICS

Mathematics

CHANCE, LUCK AND STATISTICS: THE SCIENCE OF CHANCE, Horace C. Levinson. Theory of probability and science of statistics in simple, non-technical language. Part I deals with theory of probability, covering odd superstitions in regard to "luck," the meaning of betting odds, the law of mathematical expectation, gambling, and applications in poker, roulette, lotteries, dice, bridge, and other games of chance. Part II discusses the misuse of statistics, the concept of statistical probabilities, normal and skew frequency distributions, and statistics applied to various fields—birth rates, stock speculation, insurance rates, advertising, etc. "Presented in an easy humorous style which I consider the best kind of expository writing," Prof. A. C. Cohen, Industry Quality Control. Enlarged revised edition. Formerly titled "The Science of Chance." Preface and two new appendices by the author. Index. xiv + 365pp. 5⅜ x 8. T1007 Paperbound **$1.85**

PROBABILITIES AND LIFE, Emile Borel. Translated by M. Baudin. Non-technical, highly readable introduction to the results of probability as applied to everyday situations. Partial contents: Fallacies About Probabilities Concerning Life After Death; Negligible Probabilities and the Probabilities of Everyday Life; Events of Small Probability; Application of Probabilities to Certain Problems of Heredity; Probabilities of Deaths, Diseases, and Accidents; On Poisson's Formula. Index. 3 Appendices of statistical studies and tables. vi + 87pp. 5⅜ x 8½. T121 Paperbound **$1.00**

GREAT IDEAS OF MODERN MATHEMATICS: THEIR NATURE AND USE, Jagjit Singh. Reader with only high school math will understand main mathematical ideas of modern physics, astronomy, genetics, psychology, evolution, etc., better than many who use them as tools, but comprehend little of their basic structure. Author uses his wide knowledge of non-mathematical fields in brilliant exposition of differential equations, matrices, group theory, logic, statistics, problems of mathematical foundations, imaginary numbers, vectors, etc. Original publication. 2 appendices. 2 indexes. 65 illustr. 322pp. 5⅜ x 8. S587 Paperbound **$1.75**

MATHEMATICS IN ACTION, O. G. Sutton. Everyone with a command of high school algebra will find this book one of the finest possible introductions to the application of mathematics to physical theory. Ballistics, numerical analysis, waves and wavelike phenomena, Fourier series, group concepts, fluid flow and aerodynamics, statistical measures, and meteorology are discussed with unusual clarity. Some calculus and differential equations theory is developed by the author for the reader's help in the more difficult sections. 88 figures. Index. viii + 236pp. 5⅜ x 8. T440 Clothbound **$3.50**

THE FOURTH DIMENSION SIMPLY EXPLAINED, edited by H. P. Manning. 22 essays, originally Scientific American contest entries, that use a minimum of mathematics to explain aspects of 4-dimensional geometry: analogues to 3-dimensional space, 4-dimensional absurdities and curiosities (such as removing the contents of an egg without puncturing its shell), possible measurements and forms, etc. Introduction by the editor. Only book of its sort on a truly elementary level, excellent introduction to advanced works. 82 figures. 251pp. 5⅜ x 8. T711 Paperbound **$1.35**

MATHEMATICS—INTERMEDIATE TO ADVANCED

General

INTRODUCTION TO APPLIED MATHEMATICS, Francis D. Murnaghan. A practical and thoroughly sound introduction to a number of advanced branches of higher mathematics. Among the selected topics covered in detail are: vector and matrix analysis, partial and differential equations, integral equations, calculus of variations, Laplace transform theory, the vector triple product, linear vector functions, quadratic and bilinear forms, Fourier series, spherical harmonics, Bessel functions, the Heaviside expansion formula, and many others. Extremely useful book for graduate students in physics, engineering, chemistry, and mathematics. Index. 111 study exercises with answers. 41 illustrations. ix + 389pp. 5⅜ x 8½.
S1042 Paperbound **$2.00**

OPERATIONAL METHODS IN APPLIED MATHEMATICS, H. S. Carslaw and J. C. Jaeger. Explanation of the application of the Laplace Transformation to differential equations, a simple and effective substitute for more difficult and obscure operational methods. Of great practical value to engineers and to all workers in applied mathematics. Chapters on: Ordinary Linear Differential Equations with Constant Coefficients;; Electric Circuit Theory; Dynamical Applications; The Inversion Theorem for the Laplace Transformation; Conduction of Heat; Vibrations of Continuous Mechanical Systems; Hydrodynamics; Impulsive Functions; Chains of Differential Equations; and other related matters. 3 appendices. 153 problems, many with answers. 22 figures. xvi + 359pp. 5⅜ x 8½.
S1011 Paperbound **$2.25**

APPLIED MATHEMATICS FOR RADIO AND COMMUNICATIONS ENGINEERS, C. E. Smith. No extraneous material here!—only the theories, equations, and operations essential and immediately useful for radio work. Can be used as refresher, as handbook of applications and tables, or as full home-study course. Ranges from simplest arithmetic through calculus, series, and wave forms, hyperbolic trigonometry, simultaneous equations in mesh circuits, etc. Supplies applications right along with each math topic discussed. 22 useful tables of functions, formulas, logs, etc. Index. 166 exercises, 140 examples, all with answers. 95 diagrams. Bibliography. x + 336pp. 5⅜ x 8.
S141 Paperbound **$1.75**

Algebra, group theory, determinants, sets, matrix theory

ALGEBRAS AND THEIR ARITHMETICS, L. E. Dickson. Provides the foundation and background necessary to any advanced undergraduate or graduate student studying abstract algebra. Begins with elementary introduction to linear transformations, matrices, field of complex numbers; proceeds to order, basal units, modulus, quaternions, etc.; develops calculus of linears sets, describes various examples of algebras including invariant, difference, nilpotent, semi-simple. "Makes the reader marvel at his genius for clear and profound analysis," Amer. Mathematical Monthly. Index. xii + 241pp. 5⅜ x 8.
S616 Paperbound **$1.50**

THE THEORY OF EQUATIONS WITH AN INTRODUCTION TO THE THEORY OF BINARY ALGEBRAIC FORMS, W. S. Burnside and A. W. Panton. Extremely thorough and concrete discussion of the theory of equations, with extensive detailed treatment of many topics curtailed in later texts. Covers theory of algebraic equations, properties of polynomials, symmetric functions, derived functions, Horner's process, complex numbers and the complex variable, determinants and methods of elimination, invariant theory (nearly 100 pages), transformations, introduction to Galois theory, Abelian equations, and much more. Invaluable supplementary work for modern students and teachers. 759 examples and exercises. Index in each volume. Two volume set. Total of xxiv + 604pp. 5⅜ x 8.
S714 Vol I Paperbound **$1.85**
S715 Vol II Paperbound **$1.85**
The set **$3.70**

COMPUTATIONAL METHODS OF LINEAR ALGEBRA, V. N. Faddeeva, translated by C. D. Benster. First English translation of a unique and valuable work, the only work in English presenting a systematic exposition of the most important methods of linear algebra—classical and contemporary. Shows in detail how to derive numerical solutions of problems in mathematical physics which are frequently connected with those of linear algebra. Theory as well as individual practice. Part I surveys the mathematical background that is indispensable to what follows. Parts II and III, the conclusion, set forth the most important methods of solution, for both exact and iterative groups. One of the most outstanding and valuable features of this work is the 23 tables, double and triple checked for accuracy. These tables will not be found elsewhere. Author's preface. Translator's note. New bibliography and index. x + 252pp. 5⅜ x 8.
S424 Paperbound **$1.95**

ALGEBRAIC EQUATIONS, E. Dehn. Careful and complete presentation of Galois' theory of algebraic equations; theories of Lagrange and Galois developed in logical rather than historical form, with a more thorough exposition than in most modern books. Many concrete applications and fully-worked-out examples. Discusses basic theory (very clear exposition of the symmetric group); isomorphic, transitive, and Abelian groups; applications of Lagrange's and Galois' theories; and much more. Newly revised by the author. Index. List of Theorems. xi + 208pp. 5⅜ x 8.
S697 Paperbound **$1.45**

Differential equations, ordinary and partial; integral equations

INTRODUCTION TO THE DIFFERENTIAL EQUATIONS OF PHYSICS, L. Hopf. Especially valuable to the engineer with no math beyond elementary calculus. Emphasizing intuitive rather than formal aspects of concepts, the author covers an extensive territory. Partial contents: Law of causality, energy theorem, damped oscillations, coupling by friction, cylindrical and spherical coordinates, heat source, etc. Index. 48 figures. 160pp. 5⅜ x 8.
S120 Paperbound **$1.25**

INTRODUCTION TO THE THEORY OF LINEAR DIFFERENTIAL EQUATIONS, E. G. Poole. Authoritative discussions of important topics, with methods of solution more detailed than usual, for students with background of elementary course in differential equations. Studies existence theorems, linearly independent solutions; equations with constant coefficients; with uniform analytic coefficients; regular singularities; the hypergeometric equation; conformal representation; etc. Exercises. Index. 210pp. 5⅜ x 8.
S629 Paperbound **$1.65**

DIFFERENTIAL EQUATIONS FOR ENGINEERS, P. Franklin. Outgrowth of a course given 10 years at M. I. T. Makes most useful branch of pure math accessible for practical work. Theoretical basis of D.E.'s; solution of ordinary D.E.'s and partial derivatives arising from heat flow, steady-state temperature of a plate, wave equations; analytic functions; convergence of Fourier Series. 400 problems on electricity, vibratory systems, other topics. Formerly "Differential Equations for Electrical Engineers." Index 41 illus. 307pp. 5⅜ x 8.
S601 Paperbound **$1.65**

DIFFERENTIAL EQUATIONS, F. R. Moulton. A detailed, rigorous exposition of all the nonelementary processes of solving ordinary differential equations. Several chapters devoted to the treatment of practical problems, especially those of a physical nature, which are far more advanced than problems usually given as illustrations. Includes analytic differential equations; variations of a parameter; integrals of differential equations; analytic implicit functions; problems of elliptic motion; sine-amplitude functions; deviation of formal bodies; Cauchy-Lipschitz process; linear differential equations with periodic coefficients; differential equations in infinitely many variations; much more. Historical notes. 10 figures. 222 problems. Index. xv + 395pp. 5⅜ x 8.
S451 Paperbound **$2.00**

DIFFERENTIAL AND INTEGRAL EQUATIONS OF MECHANICS AND PHYSICS (DIE DIFFERENTIAL- UND INTEGRALGLEICHUNGEN DER MECHANIK UND PHYSIK), edited by P. Frank and R. von Mises. Most comprehensive and authoritative work on the mathematics of mathematical physics available today in the United States: the standard, definitive reference for teachers, physicists, engineers, and mathematicians—now published (in the original German) at a relatively inexpensive price for the first time! Every chapter in this 2,000-page set is by an expert in his field: Carathéodory, Courant, Frank, Mises, and a dozen others. Vol I, on mathematics, gives concise but complete coverages of advanced calculus, differential equations, integral equations, and potential, and partial differential equations. Index. xxiii + 916pp. Vol. II (physics): classical mechanics, optics, continuous mechanics, heat conduction and diffusion, the stationary and quasi-stationary electromagnetic field, electromagnetic oscillations, and wave mechanics. Index. xxiv + 1106pp. Two volume set. Each volume available separately. 5⅝ x 8⅜.
S787 Vol I Clothbound **$7.50**
S788 Vol II Clothbound **$7.50**
The set **$15.00**

LECTURES ON CAUCHY'S PROBLEM, J. Hadamard. Based on lectures given at Columbia, Rome, this discusses work of Riemann, Kirchhoff, Volterra, and the author's own research on the hyperbolic case in linear partial differential equations. It extends spherical and cylindrical waves to apply to all (normal) hyperbolic equations. Partial contents: Cauchy's problem, fundamental formula, equations with odd number, with even number of independent variables; method of descent. 32 figures. Index. iii + 316pp. 5⅜ x 8. S105 Paperbound **$1.75**

THEORY OF DIFFERENTIAL EQUATIONS, A. R. Forsyth. Out of print for over a decade, the complete 6 volumes (now bound as 3) of this monumental work represent the most comprehensive treatment of differential equations ever written. Historical presentation includes in 2500 pages every substantial development. Vol. 1, 2: EXACT EQUATIONS, PFAFF'S PROBLEM; ORDINARY EQUATIONS, NOT LINEAR: methods of Grassmann, Clebsch, Lie, Darboux; Cauchy's theorem; branch points; etc. Vol. 3, 4: ORDINARY EQUATIONS, NOT LINEAR; ORDINARY LINEAR EQUATIONS: Zeta Fuchsian functions, general theorems on algebraic integrals, Brun's theorem, equations with uniform periodic cofficients, etc. Vol. 4, 5: PARTIAL DIFFERENTIAL EQUATIONS: 2 existence-theorems, equations of theoretical dynamics, Laplace transformations, general transformation of equations of the 2nd order, much more. Indexes. Total of 2766pp. 5⅜ x 8. S576-7-8 Clothbound: the set **$15.00**

PARTIAL DIFFERENTIAL EQUATIONS OF MATHEMATICAL PHYSICS, A. G. Webster. A keystone work in the library of every mature physicist, engineer, researcher. Valuable sections on elasticity, compression theory, potential theory, theory of sound, heat conduction, wave propagation, vibration theory. Contents include: deduction of differential equations, vibrations, normal functions, Fourier's series, Cauchy's method, boundary problems, method of Riemann-Volterra. Spherical, cylindrical, ellipsoidal harmonics, applications, etc. 97 figures. vii + 440pp. 5⅜ x 8.
S263 Paperbound **$2.00**

ELEMENTARY CONCEPTS OF TOPOLOGY, P. Alexandroff. First English translation of the famous brief introduction to topology for the beginner or for the mathematician not undertaking extensive study. This unusually useful intuitive approach deals primarily with the concepts of complex, cycle, and homology, and is wholly consistent with current investigations. Ranges from basic concepts of set-theoretic topology to the concept of Betti groups. "Glowing example of harmony between intuition and thought," David Hilbert. Translated by A. E. Farley. Introduction by D. Hilbert. Index. 25 figures. 73pp. 5⅜ x 8.   S747 Paperbound **$1.00**

Number theory

INTRODUCTION TO THE THEORY OF NUMBERS, L. E. Dickson. Thorough, comprehensive approach with adequate coverage of classical literature, an introductory volume beginners can follow. Chapters on divisibility, congruences, quadratic residues & reciprocity, Diophantine equations, etc. Full treatment of binary quadratic forms without usual restriction to integral coefficients. Covers infinitude of primes, least residues, Fermat's theorem, Euler's phi function, Legendre's symbol, Gauss's lemma, automorphs, reduced forms, recent theorems of Thue & Siegel, many more. Much material not readily available elsewhere. 239 problems. Index. I figure. viii + 183pp. 5⅜ x 8.   S342 Paperbound **$1.65**

ELEMENTS OF NUMBER THEORY, I. M. Vinogradov. Detailed 1st course for persons without advanced mathematics; 95% of this book can be understood by readers who have gone no farther than high school algebra. Partial contents: divisibility theory, important number theoretical functions, congruences, primitive roots and indices, etc. Solutions to both problems and exercises. Tables of primes, indices, etc. Covers almost every essential formula in elementary number theory! Translated from Russian. 233 problems, 104 exercises. viii + 227pp. 5⅜ x 8.   S259 Paperbound **$1.60**

THEORY OF NUMBERS and DIOPHANTINE ANALYSIS, R. D. Carmichael. These two complete works in one volume form one of the most lucid introductions to number theory, requiring only a firm foundation in high school mathematics. "Theory of Numbers," partial contents: Eratosthenes' sieve, Euclid's fundamental theorem, G.C.F. and L.C.M. of two or more integers, linear congruences, etc "Diophantine Analysis": rational triangles, Pythagorean triangles, equations of third, fourth, higher degrees, method of functional equations, much more. "Theory of Numbers": 76 problems. Index. 94pp. "Diophantine Analysis": 222 problems. Index. 118pp. 5⅜ x 8.   S529 Paperbound **$1.35**

Numerical analysis, tables

MATHEMATICAL TABLES AND FORMULAS, Compiled by Robert D. Carmichael and Edwin R. Smith. Valuable collection for students, etc. Contains all tables necessary in college algebra and trigonometry, such as five-place common logarithms, logarithmic sines and tangents of small angles, logarithmic trigonometric functions, natural trigonometric functions, four-place antilogarithms, tables for changing from sexagesimal to circular and from circular to sexagesimal measure of angles, etc. Also many tables and formulas not ordinarily accessible, including powers, roots, and reciprocals, exponential and hyperbolic functions, ten-place logarithms of prime numbers, and formulas and theorems from analytical and elementary geometry and from calculus. Explanatory introduction. viii + 269pp. 5⅜ x 8½.   S111 Paperbound **$1.00**

MATHEMATICAL TABLES, H. B. Dwight. Unique for its coverage in one volume of almost every function of importance in applied mathematics, engineering, and the physical sciences. Three extremely fine tables of the three trig functions and their inverse functions to thousandths of radians; natural and common logarithms; squares, cubes; hyperbolic functions and the inverse hyperbolic functions; $(a^2 + b^2)$ exp. ½a; complete elliptic integrals of the 1st and 2nd kind; sine and cosine integrals; exponential integrals Ei(x) and Ei(−x); binomial coefficients; factorials to 250; surface zonal harmonics and first derivatives; Bernoulli and Euler numbers and their logs to base of 10; Gamma function; normal probability integral; over 60 pages of Bessel functions; the Riemann Zeta function. Each table with formulae generally used, sources of more extensive tables, interpolation data, etc. Over half have columns of differences, to facilitate interpolation. Introduction. Index. viii + 231pp. 5⅜ x 8.   S445 Paperbound **$1.75**

TABLES OF FUNCTIONS WITH FORMULAE AND CURVES, E. Jahnke & F. Emde. The world's most comprehensive 1-volume English-text collection of tables, formulae, curves of transcendent functions. 4th corrected edition, new 76-page section giving tables, formulae for elementary functions—not in other English editions. Partial contents: sine, cosine, logarithmic integral; factorial function; error integral; theta functions; elliptic integrals, functions; Legendre, Bessel, Riemann, Mathieu, hypergeometric functions, etc. Supplementary books. Bibliography. Indexed. "Out of the way functions for which we know no other source," SCIENTIFIC COMPUTING SERVICE, Ltd. 212 figures. 400pp. 5⅜ x 8.   S133 Paperbound **$2.00**

CHEMISTRY AND PHYSICAL CHEMISTRY

ORGANIC CHEMISTRY, F. C. Whitmore. The entire subject of organic chemistry for the practicing chemist and the advanced student. Storehouse of facts, theories, processes found elsewhere only in specialized journals. Covers aliphatic compounds (500 pages on the properties and synthetic preparation of hydrocarbons, halides, proteins, ketones, etc.), alicyclic compounds, aromatic compounds, heterocyclic compounds, organophosphorus and organometallic compounds. Methods of synthetic preparation analyzed critically throughout. Includes much of biochemical interest. "The scope of this volume is astonishing," INDUSTRIAL AND ENGINEERING CHEMISTRY. 12,000-reference index. 2387-item bibliography. Total of x + 1005pp. 5⅜ x 8. Two volume set.
S700 Vol I Paperbound **$2.00**
S701 Vol II Paperbound **$2.00**
The set **$4.00**

THE MODERN THEORY OF MOLECULAR STRUCTURE, Bernard Pullman. A reasonably popular account of recent developments in atomic and molecular theory. Contents: The Wave Function and Wave Equations (history and bases of present theories of molecular structure); The Electronic Structure of Atoms (Description and classification of atomic wave functions, etc.); Diatomic Molecules; Non-Conjugated Polyatomic Molecules; Conjugated Polyatomic Molecules; The Structure of Complexes. Minimum of mathematical background needed. New translation by David Antin of "La Structure Moleculaire." Index. Bibliography. vii + 87pp. 5⅜ x 8½.
S987 Paperbound **$1.00**

CATALYSIS AND CATALYSTS, Marcel Prettre, Director, Research Institute on Catalysis. This brief book, translated into English for the first time, is the finest summary of the principal modern concepts, methods, and results of catalysis. Ideal introduction for beginning chemistry and physics students. Chapters: Basic Definitions of Catalysis (true catalysis and generalization of the concept of catalysis); The Scientific Bases of Catalysis (Catalysis and chemical thermodynamics, catalysis and chemical kinetics); Homogeneous Catalysis (acid-base catalysis, etc.); Chain Reactions; Contact Masses; Heterogeneous Catalysis (Mechanisms of contact catalyses, etc.); and Industrial Applications (acids and fertilizers, petroleum and petroleum chemistry, rubber, plastics, synthetic resins, and fibers). Translated by David Antin. Index. vi + 88pp. 5⅜ x 8½.
S998 Paperbound **$1.00**

POLAR MOLECULES, Pieter Debye. This work by Nobel laureate Debye offers a complete guide to fundamental electrostatic field relations, polarizability, molecular structure. Partial contents: electric intensity, displacement and force, polarization by orientation, molar polarization and molar refraction, halogen-hydrides, polar liquids, ionic saturation, dielectric constant, etc. Special chapter considers quantum theory. Indexed. 172pp. 5⅜ x 8.
S64 Paperbound **$1.50**

THE ELECTRONIC THEORY OF ACIDS AND BASES, W. F. Luder and Saverio Zuffanti. The first full systematic presentation of the electronic theory of acids and bases—treating the theory and its ramifications in an uncomplicated manner. Chapters: Historical Background; Atomic Orbitals and Valence; The Electronic Theory of Acids and Bases; Electrophilic and Electrodotic Reagents; Acidic and Basic Radicals; Neutralization; Titrations with Indicators; Displacement; Catalysis; Acid Catalysis; Base Catalysis; Alkoxides and Catalysts; Conclusion. Required reading for all chemists. Second revised (1961) eidtion, with additional examples and references. 3 figures. 9 tables. Index. Bibliography xii + 165pp. 5⅜ x 8.
S201 Paperbound **$1.50**

KINETIC THEORY OF LIQUIDS, J. Frenkel. Regarding the kinetic theory of liquids as a generalization and extension of the theory of solid bodies, this volume covers all types of arrangements of solids, thermal displacements of atoms, interstitial atoms and ions, orientational and rotational motion of molecules, and transition between states of matter. Mathematical theory is developed close to the physical subject matter. 216 bibliographical footnotes. 55 figures. xi + 485pp. 5⅜ x 8.
S95 Paperbound **$2.55**

THE PRINCIPLES OF ELECTROCHEMISTRY, D. A. MacInnes. Basic equations for almost every subfield of electrochemistry from first principles, referring at all times to the soundest and most recent theories and results; unusually useful as text or as reference. Covers coulometers and Faraday's Law, electrolytic conductance, the Debye-Hueckel method for the theoretical calculation of activity coefficients, concentration cells, standard electrode potentials, thermodynamic ionization constants, pH, potentiometric titrations, irreversible phenomena, Planck's equation, and much more. "Excellent treatise," AMERICAN CHEMICAL SOCIETY JOURNAL. "Highly recommended," CHEMICAL AND METALLURGICAL ENGINEERING. 2 Indices. Appendix. 585-item bibliography. 137 figures. 94 tables. ii + 478pp. 5⅝ x 8⅜.
S52 Paperbound **$2.45**

THE PHASE RULE AND ITS APPLICATION, Alexander Findlay. Covering chemical phenomena of 1, 2, 3, 4, and multiple component systems, this "standard work on the subject" (NATURE, London), has been completely revised and brought up to date by A. N. Campbell and N. O. Smith. Brand new material has been added on such matters as binary, tertiary liquid equilibria, solid solutions in ternary systems, quinary systems of salts and water. Completely revised to triangular coordinates in ternary systems, clarified graphic representation, solid models, etc. 9th revised edition. Author, subject indexes. 236 figures. 505 footnotes, mostly bibliographic. xii + 494pp. 5⅜ x 8.
S91 Paperbound **$2.45**

PHYSICS

General physics

FOUNDATIONS OF PHYSICS, R. B. Lindsay & H. Margenau. Excellent bridge between semi-popular works & technical treatises. A discussion of methods of physical description, construction of theory; valuable for physicist with elementary calculus who is interested in ideas that give meaning to data, tools of modern physics. Contents include symbolism, mathematical equations; space & time foundations of mechanics; probability; physics & continua; electron theory; special & general relativity; quantum mechanics; causality. "Thorough and yet not overdetailed. Unreservedly recommended," NATURE (London). Unabridged, corrected edition. List of recommended readings. 35 illustrations. xi + 537pp. 5⅜ x 8.
S377 Paperbound **$2.75**

FUNDAMENTAL FORMULAS OF PHYSICS, ed. by D. H. Menzel. Highly useful, fully inexpensive reference and study text, ranging from simple to highly sophisticated operations. Mathematics integrated into text—each chapter stands as short textbook of field represented. Vol. 1: Statistics, Physical Constants, Special Theory of Relativity, Hydrodynamics, Aerodynamics, Boundary Value Problems in Math. Physics; Viscosity, Electromagnetic Theory, etc. Vol. 2: Sound, Acoustics, Geometrical Optics, Electron Optics, High-Energy Phenomena, Magnetism, Biophysics, much more. Index. Total of 800pp. 5⅜ x 8.   Vol. 1 S595 Paperbound **$2.00**
Vol. 2 S596 Paperbound **$2.00**

MATHEMATICAL PHYSICS, D. H. Menzel. Thorough one-volume treatment of the mathematical techniques vital for classic mechanics, electromagnetic theory, quantum theory, and relativity. Written by the Harvard Professor of Astrophysics for junior, senior, and graduate courses, it gives clear explanations of all those aspects of function theory, vectors, matrices, dyadics, tensors, partial differential equations, etc., necessary for the understanding of the various physical theories. Electron theory, relativity, and other topics seldom presented appear here in considerable detail. Scores of definitions, conversion factors, dimensional constants, etc. "More detailed than normal for an advanced text . . . excellent set of sections on Dyadics, Matrices, and Tensors," JOURNAL OF THE FRANKLIN INSTITUTE. Index. 193 problems, with answers. x + 412pp. 5⅜ x 8.   S56 Paperbound **$2.00**

THE SCIENTIFIC PAPERS OF J. WILLARD GIBBS. All the published papers of America's outstanding theoretical scientist (except for "Statistical Mechanics" and "Vector Analysis"). Vol I (thermodynamics) contains one of the most brilliant of all 19th-century scientific papers—the 300-page "On the Equilibrium of Heterogeneous Substances," which founded the science of physical chemistry, and clearly stated a number of highly important natural laws for the first time; 8 other papers complete the first volume. Vol II includes 2 papers on dynamics, 8 on vector analysis and multiple algebra, 5 on the electromagnetic theory of light, and 6 miscellaneous papers. Biographical sketch by H. A. Bumstead. Total of xxxvi + 718pp. 5⅝ x 8⅜.
S721 Vol I Paperbound **$2.00**
S722 Vol II Paperbound **$2.00**
The set **$4.00**

BASIC THEORIES OF PHYSICS, Peter Gabriel Bergmann. Two-volume set which presents a critical examination of important topics in the major subdivisions of classical and modern physics. The first volume is concerned with classical mechanics and electrodynamics: mechanics of mass points, analytical mechanics, matter in bulk, electrostatics and magnetostatics, electromagnetic interaction, the field waves, special relativity, and waves. The second volume (Heat and Quanta) contains discussions of the kinetic hypothesis, physics and statistics, stationary ensembles, laws of thermodynamics, early quantum theories, atomic spectra, probability waves, quantization in wave mechanics, approximation methods, and abstract quantum theory. A valuable supplement to any thorough course or text.
Heat and Quanta: Index. 8 figures. x + 300pp. 5⅜ x 8½.   S968 Paperbound **$1.75**
Mechanics and Electrodynamics: Index. 14 figures. vii + 280pp. 5⅜ x 8½.
S969 Paperbound **$1.75**

THEORETICAL PHYSICS, A. S. Kompaneyets. One of the very few thorough studies of the subject in this price range. Provides advanced students with a comprehensive theoretical background. Especially strong on recent experimentation and developments in quantum theory. Contents: Mechanics (Generalized Coordinates, Lagrange's Equation, Collision of Particles, etc.), Electrodynamics (Vector Analysis, Maxwell's equations, Transmission of Signals, Theory of Relativity, etc.), Quantum Mechanics (the Inadequacy of Classical Mechanics, the Wave Equation, Motion in a Central Field, Quantum Theory of Radiation, Quantum Theories of Dispersion and Scattering, etc.), and Statistical Physics (Equilibrium Distribution of Molecules in an Ideal Gas, Boltzmann statistics, Bose and Fermi Distribution, Thermodynamic Quantities, etc.). Revised to 1961. Translated by George Yankovsky, authorized by Kompaneyets. 137 exercises. 56 figures. 529pp. 5⅜ x 8½. S972 Paperbound **$2.50**

ANALYTICAL AND CANONICAL FORMALISM IN PHYSICS, André Mercier. A survey, in one volume, of the variational principles (the key principles—in mathematical form—from which the basic laws of any one branch of physics can be derived) of the several branches of physical theory, together with an examination of the relationships among them. Contents: the Lagrangian Formalism, Lagrangian Densities, Canonical Formalism, Canonical Form of Electrodynamics, Hamiltonian Densities, Transformations, and Canonical Form with Vanishing Jacobian Determinant. Numerous examples and exercises. For advanced students, teachers, etc. 6 figures. Index. viii + 222pp. 5⅜ x 8½.   S1077 Paperbound **$1.75**

MATHEMATICAL PUZZLES AND RECREATIONS

AMUSEMENTS IN MATHEMATICS, Henry Ernest Dudeney. The foremost British originator of mathematical puzzles is always intriguing, witty, and paradoxical in this classic, one of the largest collections of mathematical amusements. More than 430 puzzles, problems, and paradoxes. Mazes and games, problems on number manipulation, unicursal and other route problems, puzzles on measuring, weighing, packing, age, kinship, chessboards, joining, crossing river, plane figure dissection, and many others. Solutions. More than 450 illustrations. vii + 258pp. 5⅜ x 8.   T473 Paperbound **$1.25**

SYMBOLIC LOGIC and THE GAME OF LOGIC, Lewis Carroll. "Symbolic Logic" is not concerned with modern symbolic logic, but is instead a collection of over 380 problems posed with charm and imagination, using the syllogism, and a fascinating diagrammatic method of drawing conclusions. In "The Game of Logic," Carroll's whimsical imagination devises a logical game played with 2 diagrams and counters (included) to manipulate hundreds of tricky syllogisms. The final section, "Hit or Miss" is a lagniappe of 101 additional puzzles in the delightful Carroll manner. Until this reprint edition, both of these books were rarities costing up to $15 each. Symbolic Logic: Index, xxxi + 199pp. The Game of Logic: 96pp. Two vols. bound as one. 5⅜ x 8.   T492 Paperbound **$1.50**

MAZES AND LABYRINTHS: A BOOK OF PUZZLES, W. Shepherd. Mazes, formerly associated with mystery and ritual, are still among the most intriguing of intellectual puzzles. This is a novel and different collection of 50 amusements that embody the principle of the maze: mazes in the classical tradition; 3-dimensional, ribbon, and Möbius-strip mazes; hidden messages; spatial arrangements; etc.—almost all built on amusing story situations. 84 illustrations. Essay on maze psychology. Solutions. xv + 122pp. 5⅜ x 8.   T731 Paperbound **$1.00**

MATHEMATICAL RECREATIONS, M. Kraitchik. Some 250 puzzles, problems, demonstrations of recreational mathematics for beginners & advanced mathematicians. Unusual historical problems from Greek, Medieval, Arabic, Hindu sources: modern problems based on "mathematics without numbers," geometry, topology, arithmetic, etc. Pastimes derived from figurative numbers, Mersenne numbers, Fermat numbers; fairy chess, latruncles, reversi, many topics. Full solutions. Excellent for insights into special fields of math. 181 illustrations. 330pp. 5⅜ x 8.   T163 Paperbound **$1.75**

MATHEMATICAL PUZZLES OF SAM LOYD, Vol. I, selected and edited by M. Gardner. Puzzles by the greatest puzzle creator and innovator. Selected from his famous "Cyclopedia of Puzzles," they retain the unique style and historical flavor of the originals. There are posers based on arithmetic, algebra, probability, game theory, route tracing, topology, counter, sliding block, operations research, geometrical dissection. Includes his famous "14-15" puzzle which was a national craze, and his "Horse of a Different Color" which sold millions of copies. 117 of his most ingenious puzzles in all, 120 line drawings and diagrams. Solutions. Selected references. xx + 167pp. 5⅜ x 8.   T498 Paperbound **$1.00**

MY BEST PUZZLES IN MATHEMATICS, Hubert Phillips ("Caliban"). Caliban is generally considered the best of the modern problemists. Here are 100 of his best and wittiest puzzles, selected by the author himself from such publications as the London Daily Telegraph, and each puzzle is guaranteed to put even the sharpest puzzle detective through his paces. Perfect for the development of clear thinking and a logical mind. Complete solutions are provided for every puzzle. x + 107pp. 5⅜ x 8½.   T91 Paperbound **$1.00**

MY BEST PUZZLES IN LOGIC AND REASONING, H. Phillips ("Caliban"). 100 choice, hitherto unavailable puzzles by England's best-known problemist. No special knowledge needed to solve these logical or inferential problems, just an unclouded mind, nerves of steel, and fast reflexes. Data presented are both necessary and just sufficient to allow one unambiguous answer. More than 30 different types of puzzles, all ingenious and varied, many one of a kind, that will challenge the expert, please the beginner. Original publication. 100 puzzles, full solutions. x + 107pp. 5⅜ x 8½.   T119 Paperbound **$1.00**

MATHEMATICAL PUZZLES FOR BEGINNERS AND ENTHUSIASTS, G. Mott-Smith. 188 mathematical puzzles to test mental agility. Inference, interpretation, algebra, dissection of plane figures, geometry, properties of numbers, decimation, permutations, probability, all enter these delightful problems. Puzzles like the Odic Force, How to Draw an Ellipse, Spider's Cousin, more than 180 others. Detailed solutions. Appendix with square roots, triangular numbers, primes, etc. 135 illustrations. 2nd revised edition. 248pp. 5⅜ x 8.   T198 Paperbound **$1.00**

MATHEMATICS, MAGIC AND MYSTERY, Martin Gardner. Card tricks, feats of mental mathematics, stage mind-reading, other "magic" explained as applications of probability, sets, theory of numbers, topology, various branches of mathematics. Creative examination of laws and their applications with scores of new tricks and insights. 115 sections discuss tricks wtih cards, dice, coins; geometrical vanishing tricks, dozens of others. No sleight of hand needed; mathematics guarantees success. 115 illustrations. xii + 174pp. 5⅜ x 8.
T335 Paperbound **$1.00**

RECREATIONS IN THE THEORY OF NUMBERS: THE QUEEN OF MATHEMATICS ENTERTAINS, Albert H. Beiler. The theory of numbers is often referred to as the "Queen of Mathematics." In this book Mr. Beiler has compiled the first English volume to deal exclusively with the recreational aspects of number theory, an inherently recreational branch of mathematics. The author's clear style makes for enjoyable reading as he deals with such topics as: perfect numbers, amicable numbers, Fermat's theorem, Wilson's theorem, interesting properties of digits, methods of factoring, primitive roots, Euler's function, polygonal and figurate numbers, Mersenne numbers, congruence, repeating decimals, etc. Countless puzzle problems, with full answers and explanations. For mathematicians and mathematically-inclined laymen, etc. New publication. 28 figures. 9 illustrations. 103 tables. Bibliography at chapter ends. vi + 247pp. 5⅜ x 8½. **T1096 Paperbound $1.85**

PAPER FOLDING FOR BEGINNERS, W. D. Murray and F. J. Rigney. A delightful introduction to the varied and entertaining Japanese art of origami (paper folding), with a full crystal-clear text that anticipates every difficulty; over 275 clearly labeled diagrams of all important stages in creation. You get results at each stage, since complex figures are logically developed from simpler ones. 43 different pieces are explained: place mats, drinking cups, bonbon boxes, sailboats, frogs, roosters, etc. 6 photographic plates. 279 diagrams. 95pp. 5⅝ x 8⅜. **T713 Paperbound $1.00**

1800 RIDDLES, ENIGMAS AND CONUNDRUMS, Darwin A. Hindman. Entertaining collection ranging from hilarious gags to outrageous puns to sheer nonsense—a welcome respite from sophisticated humor. Children, toastmasters, and practically anyone with a funny bone will find these zany riddles tickling and eminently repeatable. Sample: "Why does Santa Claus always go down the chimney?" "Because it soots him." Some old, some new—covering a wide variety of subjects. New publication. iii + 154pp. 5⅜ x 8½. **T1059 Paperbound $1.00**

EASY-TO-DO ENTERTAINMENTS AND DIVERSIONS WITH CARDS, STRING, COINS, PAPER AND MATCHES, R. M. Abraham. Over 300 entertaining games, tricks, puzzles, and pastimes for children and adults. Invaluable to anyone in charge of groups of youngsters, for party givers, etc. Contains sections on card tricks and games, making things by paperfolding—toys, decorations, and the like; tricks with coins, matches, and pieces of string; descriptions of games; toys that can be made from common household objects; mathematical recreations; word games; and 50 miscellaneous entertainments. Formerly "Winter Nights Entertainments." Introduction by Lord Baden Powell. 329 illustrations. v + 186pp. 5⅜ x 8. **T921 Paperbound $1.00**

DIVERSIONS AND PASTIMES WITH CARDS, STRING, PAPER AND MATCHES, R. M. Abraham. Another collection of amusements and diversion for game and puzzle fans of all ages. Many new paperfolding ideas and tricks, an extensive section on amusements with knots and splices, two chapters of easy and not-so-easy problems, coin and match tricks, and lots of other parlor pastimes from the agile mind of the late British problemist and gamester. Corrected and revised version. Illustrations. 160pp. 5⅜ x 8½. **T1127 Paperbound $1.00**

STRING FIGURES AND HOW TO MAKE THEM: A STUDY OF CAT'S-CRADLE IN MANY LANDS, Caroline Furness Jayne. In a simple and easy-to-follow manner, this book describes how to make 107 different string figures. Not only is looping and crossing string between the fingers a common youthful diversion, but it is an ancient form of amusement practiced in all parts of the globe, especially popular among primitive tribes. These games are fun for all ages and offer an excellent means for developing manual dexterity and coordination. Much insight also for the anthropological observer on games and diversions in many different cultures. Index. Bibliography. Introduction by A. C. Haddon, Cambridge University. 17 full-page plates. 950 illustrations. xxiii + 407pp. 5⅜ x 8½. **T152 Paperbound $2.00**

CRYPTANALYSIS, Helen F. Gaines. (Formerly ELEMENTARY CRYPTANALYSIS.) A standard elementary and intermediate text for serious students. It does not confine itself to old material, but contains much that is not generally known, except to experts. Concealment, Transposition, Substitution ciphers; Vigenère, Kasiski, Playfair, multafid, dozens of other techniques. Appendix with sequence charts, letter frequencies in English, 5 other languages, English word frequencies. Bibliography. 167 codes. New to this edition: solution to codes. vi + 230pp. 5⅜ x 8. **T97 Paperbound $1.95**

MAGIC SQUARES AND CUBES, W. S. Andrews. Only book-length treatment in English, a thorough non-technical description and analysis. Here are nasik, overlapping, pandiagonal, serrated squares; magic circles, cubes, spheres, rhombuses. Try your hand at 4-dimensional magical figures! Much unusual folklore and tradition included. High school algebra is sufficient. 754 diagrams and illustrations. viii + 419pp. 5⅜ x 8. **T658 Paperbound $1.85**

CALIBAN'S PROBLEM BOOK: MATHEMATICAL, INFERENTIAL, AND CRYPTOGRAPHIC PUZZLES, H. Phillips ("Caliban"), S. T. Shovelton, G. S. Marshall. 105 ingenious problems by the greatest living creator of puzzles based on logic and inference. Rigorous, modern, piquant, and reflecting their author's unusual personality, these intermediate and advanced puzzles all involve the ability to reason clearly through complex situations; some call for mathematical knowledge, ranging from algebra to number theory. Solutions. xi + 180pp. 5⅜ x 8. **T736 Paperbound $1.25**

FICTION

THE LAND THAT TIME FORGOT and THE MOON MAID, Edgar Rice Burroughs. In the opinion of many, Burroughs' best work. The first concerns a strange island where evolution is individual rather than phylogenetic. Speechless anthropoids develop into intelligent human beings within a single generation. The second projects the reader far into the future and describes the first voyage to the Moon (in the year 2025), the conquest of the Earth by the Moon, and years of violence and adventure as the enslaved Earthmen try to regain possession of their planet. "An imaginative tour de force that keeps the reader keyed up and expectant," NEW YORK TIMES. Complete, unabridged text of the original two novels (three parts in each). 5 illustrations by J. Allen St. John. vi + 552pp. 5⅜ x 8½.
T1020 Clothbound **$3.75**
T358 Paperbound **$2.00**

AT THE EARTH'S CORE, PELLUCIDAR, TANAR OF PELLUCIDAR: THREE SCIENCE FICTION NOVELS BY EDGAR RICE BURROUGHS. Complete, unabridged texts of the first three Pellucidar novels. Tales of derring-do by the famous master of science fiction. The locale for these three related stories is the inner surface of the hollow Earth where we discover the world of Pellucidar, complete with all types of bizarre, menacing creatures, strange peoples, and alluring maidens—guaranteed to delight all Burroughs fans and a wide circle of adventure lovers. Illustrated by J. Allen St. John and P. F. Berdanier. vi + 433pp. 5⅜ x 8½.
T1051 Paperbound **$2.00**

THE PIRATES OF VENUS and LOST ON VENUS: TWO VENUS NOVELS BY EDGAR RICE BURROUGHS. Two related novels, complete and unabridged. Exciting adventure on the planet Venus with Earthman Carson Napier broken-field running through one dangerous episode after another. All lovers of swashbuckling science fiction will enjoy these two stories set in a world of fascinating societies, fierce beasts, 5000-ft. trees, lush vegetation, and wide seas. Illustrations by Fortunino Matania. Total of vi + 340pp. 5⅜ x 8½. T1053 Paperbound **$1.75**

A PRINCESS OF MARS and A FIGHTING MAN OF MARS: TWO MARTIAN NOVELS BY EDGAR RICE BURROUGHS. "Princess of Mars" is the very first of the great Martian novels written by Burroughs, and it is probably the best of them all; it set the pattern for all of his later fantasy novels and contains a thrilling cast of strange peoples and creatures and the formula of Olympian heroism amidst ever-fluctuating fortunes which Burroughs carries off so successfully. "Fighting Man" returns to the same scenes and cities—many years later. A mad scientist, a degenerate dictator, and an indomitable defender of the right clash—with the fate of the Red Planet at stake! Complete, unabridged reprinting of original editions. Illustrations by F. E. Schoonover and Hugh Hutton. v + 356pp. 5⅜ x 8½.
T1140 Paperbound **$1.75**

THREE MARTIAN NOVELS, Edgar Rice Burroughs. Contains: Thuvia, Maid of Mars; The Chessmen of Mars; and The Master Mind of Mars. High adventure set in an imaginative and intricate conception of the Red Planet. Mars is peopled with an intelligent, heroic human race which lives in densely populated cities and with fierce barbarians who inhabit dead sea bottoms. Other exciting creatures abound amidst an inventive framework of Martian history and geography. Complete unabridged reprintings of the first edition. 16 illustrations by J. Allen St. John. vi + 499pp. 5⅜ x 8½. T39 Paperbound **$1.85**

THREE PROPHETIC NOVELS BY H. G. WELLS, edited by E. F. Bleiler. Complete texts of "When the Sleeper Wakes" (1st book printing in 50 years), "A Story of the Days to Come," "The Time Machine" (1st complete printing in book form). Exciting adventures in the future are as enjoyable today as 50 years ago when first printed. Predict TV, movies, intercontinental airplanes, prefabricated houses, air-conditioned cities, etc. First important author to foresee problems of mind control, technological dictatorships. "Absolute best of imaginative fiction," N. Y. Times. Introduction. 335pp. 5⅜ x 8. T605 Paperbound **$1.50**

28 SCIENCE FICTION STORIES OF H. G. WELLS. Two full unabridged novels, MEN LIKE GODS and STAR BEGOTTEN, plus 26 short stories by the master science-fiction writer of all time. Stories of space, time, invention, exploration, future adventure—an indispensable part of the library of everyone interested in science and adventure. PARTIAL CONTENTS: Men Like Gods, The Country of the Blind, In the Abyss, The Crystal Egg, The Man Who Could Work Miracles, A Story of the Days to Come, The Valley of Spiders, and 21 more! 928pp. 5⅜ x 8.
T265 Clothbound **$4.50**

THE WAR IN THE AIR, IN THE DAYS OF THE COMET, THE FOOD OF THE GODS: THREE SCIENCE FICTION NOVELS BY H. G. WELLS. Three exciting Wells offerings bearing on vital social and philosophical issues of his and our own day. Here are tales of air power, strategic bombing, East vs. West, the potential miracles of science, the potential disasters from outer space, the relationship between scientific advancement and moral progress, etc. First reprinting of "War in the Air" in almost 50 years. An excellent sampling of Wells at his storytelling best. Complete, unabridged reprintings. 16 illustrations. 645pp. 5⅜ x 8½.
T1135 Paperbound **$2.00**

SEVEN SCIENCE FICTION NOVELS, H. G. Wells. Full unabridged texts of 7 science-fiction novels of the master. Ranging from biology, physics, chemistry, astronomy to sociology and other studies, Mr. Wells extrapolates whole worlds of strange and intriguing character. "One will have to go far to match this for entertainment, excitement, and sheer pleasure . . . ," NEW YORK TIMES. Contents: The Time Machine, The Island of Dr. Moreau, First Men in the Moon, The Invisible Man, The War of the Worlds, The Food of the Gods, In the Days of the Comet. 1015pp. 5⅜ x 8.   T264 Clothbound **$4.50**

BEST GHOST STORIES OF J. S. LE FANU, Selected and introduced by E. F. Bleiler. LeFanu is deemed the greatest name in Victorian supernatural fiction. Here are 16 of his best horror stories, including 2 nouvelles: "Carmilla," a classic vampire tale couched in a perverse eroticism, and "The Haunted Baronet." Also: "Sir Toby's Will," "Green Tea," "Schalken the Painter," "Ultor de Lacy," "The Familiar," etc. The first American publication of about half of this material: a long-overdue opportunity to get a choice sampling of LeFanu's work. New selection (1964). 8 illustrations. 5⅜ x 8⅜.   T415 Paperbound **$1.85**

THE WONDERFUL WIZARD OF OZ, L. F. Baum. Only edition in print with all the original W. W. Denslow illustrations in full color—as much a part of "The Wizard" as Tenniel's drawings are for "Alice in Wonderland." "The Wizard" is still America's best-loved fairy tale, in which, as the author expresses it, "The wonderment and joy are retained and the heartaches and nightmares left out." Now today's young readers can enjoy every word and wonderful picture of the original book. New introduction by Martin Gardner. A Baum bibliography. 23 full-page color plates. viii + 268pp. 5⅜ x 8.   T691 Paperbound **$1.45**

GHOST AND HORROR STORIES OF AMBROSE BIERCE, Selected and introduced by E. F. Bleiler. 24 morbid, eerie tales—the cream of Bierce's fiction output. Contains such memorable pieces as "The Moonlit Road," "The Damned Thing," "An Inhabitant of Carcosa," "The Eyes of the Panther," "The Famous Gilson Bequest," "The Middle Toe of the Right Foot," and other chilling stories, plus the essay, "Visions of the Night" in which Bierce gives us a kind of rationale for his aesthetic of horror. New collection (1964). xxii + 199pp. 5⅜ x 8⅜.   T767 Paperbound **$1.00**

HUMOR

MR. DOOLEY ON IVRYTHING AND IVRYBODY, Finley Peter Dunne. Since the time of his appearance in 1893, "Mr. Dooley," the fictitious Chicago bartender, has been recognized as America's most humorous social and political commentator. Collected in this volume are 102 of the best Dooley pieces—all written around the turn of the century, the height of his popularity. Mr. Dooley's Irish brogue is employed wittily and penetratingly on subjects which are just as fresh and relevant today as they were then: corruption and hypocrisy of politicans, war preparations and chauvinism, automation, Latin American affairs, superbombs, etc. Other articles range from Rudyard Kipling to football. Selected with an introduction by Robert Hutchinson. xii + 244pp. 5⅜ x 8½.   T626 Paperbound **$1.00**

RUTHLESS RHYMES FOR HEARTLESS HOMES and MORE RUTHLESS RHYMES FOR HEARTLESS HOMES, Harry Graham ("Col. D. Streamer"). A collection of Little Willy and 48 other poetic "disasters." Graham's funniest and most disrespectful verse, accompanied by original illustrations. Nonsensical, wry humor which employs stern parents, careless nurses, uninhibited children, practical jokers, single-minded golfers, Scottish lairds, etc. in the leading roles. A precursor of the "sick joke" school of today. This volume contains, bound together for the first time, two of the most perennially popular books of humor in England and America. Index. vi + 69pp. 5⅜ x 8.   T930 Paperbound **75¢**

A WHIMSEY ANTHOLOGY, Collected by Carolyn Wells. 250 of the most amusing rhymes ever written. Acrostics, anagrams, palindromes, alphabetical jingles, tongue twisters, echo verses, alliterative verses, riddles, mnemonic rhymes, interior rhymes, over 40 limericks, etc. by Lewis Carroll, Edward Lear, Joseph Addison, W. S. Gilbert, Christina Rossetti, Chas. Lamb, James Boswell, Hood, Dickens, Swinburne, Leigh Hunt, Harry Graham, Poe, Eugene Field, and many others. xiv + 221pp. 5⅜ x 8½.   T195 Paperbound **$1.25**

MY PIOUS FRIENDS AND DRUNKEN COMPANIONS and MORE PIOUS FRIENDS AND DRUNKEN COMPANIONS, Songs and ballads of Conviviality Collected by Frank Shay. Magnificently illuminated by John Held, Jr. 132 ballads, blues, vaudeville numbers, drinking songs, cowboy songs, sea chanties, comedy songs, etc. of the Naughty Nineties and early 20th century. Over a third are reprinted with music. Many perennial favorites such as: The Band Played On, Frankie and Johnnie, The Old Grey Mare, The Face on the Bar-room Floor, etc. Many others unlocatable elsewhere: The Dog-Catcher's Child, The Cannibal Maiden, Don't Go in the Lion's Cage Tonight, Mother, etc. Complete verses and introductions to songs. Unabridged republication of first editions, 2 Indexes (song titles and first lines and choruses). Introduction by Frank Shay. 2 volumes bounds as 1. Total of xvi + 235pp. 5⅜ x 8½.   T946 Paperbound **$1.00**

MAX AND MORITZ, Wilhelm Busch. Edited and annotated by H. Arthur Klein. Translated by H. Arthur Klein, M. C. Klein, and others. The mischievous high jinks of Max and Moritz, Peter and Paul, Ker and Plunk, etc. are delightfully captured in sketch and rhyme. (Companion volume to "Hypocritical Helena.") In addition to the title piece, it contians: Ker and Plunk; Two Dogs and Two Boys; The Egghead and the Two Cut-ups of Corinth; Deceitful Henry; The Boys and the Pipe; Cat and Mouse; and others. (Original German text with accompanying English translations.) Afterword by H. A. Klein. vi + 216pp. 5⅜ x 8½.
T181 Paperbound **$1.00**

THROUGH THE ALIMENTARY CANAL WITH GUN AND CAMERA: A FASCINATING TRIP TO THE INTERIOR, Personally Conducted by George S. Chappell. In mock-travelogue style, the amusing account of an imaginative journey down the alimentary canal. The "explorers" enter the esophagus, round the Adam's Apple, narrowly escape from a fierce Amoeba, struggle through the impenetrable Nerve Forests of the Lumbar Region, etc. Illustrated by the famous cartoonist, Otto Soglow, the book is as much a brilliant satire of academic pomposity and professional travel literature as it is a clever use of the facts of physiology for supremely comic purposes. Preface by Robert Benchley. Author's Foreword. 1 Photograph. 17 illustrations by O. Soglow. xii + 114pp. 5⅜ x 8½.
T376 Paperbound **$1.00**

THE BAD CHILD'S BOOK OF BEASTS, MORE BEASTS FOR WORSE CHILDREN, and A MORAL ALPHABET, H. Belloc. Hardly an anthology of humorous verse has appeared in the last 50 years without at least a couple of these famous nonsense verses. But one must see the entire volumes—with all the delightful original illustrations by Sir Basil Blackwood—to appreciate fully Belloc's charming and witty verses that play so subacidly on the platitudes of life and morals that beset his day—and ours. A great humor classic. Three books in one. Total of 157pp. 5⅜ x 8.
T749 Paperbound **$1.00**

THE DEVIL'S DICTIONARY, Ambrose Bierce. Sardonic and irreverent barbs puncturing the pomposities and absurdities of American politics, business, religion, literature, and arts, by the country's greatest satirist in the classic tradition. Epigrammatic as Shaw, piercing as Swift, American as Mark Twain, Will Rogers, and Fred Allen. Bierce will always remain the favorite of a small coterie of enthusiasts, and of writers and speakers whom he supplies with "some of the most gorgeous witticisms of the English language." (H. L. Mencken.) Over 1000 entries in alphabetical order. 144pp. 5⅜ x 8.
T487 Paperbound **$1.00**

THE COMPLETE NONSENSE OF EDWARD LEAR. This is the only complete edition of this master of gentle madness available at a popular price. A BOOK OF NONSENSE, NONSENSE SONGS, MORE NONSENSE SONGS AND STORIES in their entirety with all the old favorites that have delighted children and adults for years. The Dong With A Luminous Nose, The Jumblies, The Owl and the Pussycat, and hundreds of other bits of wonderful nonsense. 214 limericks, 3 sets of Nonsense Botany, 5 Nonsense Alphabets. 546 drawings by Lear himself, and much more. 320pp. 5⅜ x 8.
T167 Paperbound

SINGULAR TRAVELS, CAMPAIGNS, AND ADVENTURES OF BARON MUNCHAUSEN, R. E. with 90 illustrations by Gustave Doré. The first edition in over 150 years to reesta the deeds of the Prince of Liars exactly as Raspe first recorded them in 1785—the ge Baron Munchausen, one of the most popular personalities in English literature. In also are the best of the many sequels, written by other hands. Introduction on Ras J. Carswell. Bibliography of early editions. xliv + 192pp. 5⅜ x 8. T698 Paperbound **$1.00**

HOW TO TELL THE BIRDS FROM THE FLOWERS, R. W. Wood. How not to confuse a carrot with a parrot, a grape with an ape, a puffin with nuffin. Delightful drawings, clever puns, absurd little poems point out farfetched resemblances in nature. The author was a leading physicist. Introduction by Margaret Wood White. 106 illus. 60pp. 5⅜ x 8.
T523 Paperbound **75¢**

JOE MILLER'S JESTS OR, THE WITS VADE-MECUM. The original Joe Miller jest book. Gives a keen and pungent impression of life in 18th-century England. Many are somewhat on the bawdy side and they are still capable of provoking amusement and good fun. This volume is a facsimile of the original "Joe Miller" first published in 1739. It remains the most popular and influential humor book of all time. New introduction by Robert Hutchinson. xxi + 70pp. 5⅜ x 8½.
T423 Paperbound **$1.00**

Prices subject to change without notice.

Dover publishes books on art, music, philosophy, literature, languages, history, social sciences, psychology, handcrafts, orientalia, puzzles and entertainments, chess, pets and gardens, books explaining science, intermediate and higher mathematics, mathematical physics, engineering, biological sciences, earth sciences, classics of science, etc. Write to:

Dept. catrr.
Dover Publications, Inc.
180 Varick Street, N.Y. 14, N.Y.